Core Knowledge Language Arts®

Unit 11
Workbook

Skills Strand
GRADE 3

Amplify learning.

Core Knowledge®

Unit 11
Workbook

This Workbook contains worksheets that accompany the lessons from the Teacher Guide for Unit 11. Each worksheet is identified by its lesson number and where it is intended to be used. For example, if there are two worksheets for Lesson 8, the first will be numbered 8.1 and the second 8.2. The Workbook is a student component, which means each student should have a Workbook.

Anticipation Guide for
"Living Things and Their Habitats"

| Before Reading | | Statement | After Reading | | |
True	False		True	False	Page
		Ecology is about nature and life.			
		Flowers depend only on bees to spread their pollen.			
		A squirrel's favorite food is candy.			
		Acorns are candy.			
		Squirrels always remember where every acorn is buried.			

1. What is the main idea of this chapter?

    A. Living things depend on each other.

    B. Toads eat insects.

    C. Ecologists like to study.

    D. Flowers like bees to sniff their petals.

2. What would happen to oak trees if, suddenly, there were no more squirrels?

    _____

    _____

    _____

Dear Family Member,

Please help your child succeed in spelling by taking a few minutes each evening to review the words together. Helpful activities for your child to do include: spelling the words orally, writing sentences using the words, or simply copying the words.

Spelling Words

This week, we are reviewing the spelling patterns of /aw/ spelled 'au', 'aw', 'al', 'ough', and 'augh' that your child studied in Grade 2. On Friday, your child will be assessed on these words.

Students have been assigned two Challenge Words, *question* and *always*. Challenge Words are words used very often. The Challenge Word *question* does not follow the spelling pattern for this week and needs to be memorized. The Challenge Word *always* does follow the pattern for /aw/ spelled 'al'.

The Content Word for this week is *ecology*. This word is directly related to the material that we are reading in *Introduction to Ecology*. The Content Word is an optional spelling word for your child. If your child would like to try it but gets it incorrect, it will not count against him or her on the assessment. We encourage everyone to stretch themselves a bit and try to spell this word.

The spelling words, including the Challenge Words and the Content Word, are listed below:

1.	author	12.	already
2.	squawked	13.	caution
3.	dawdle	14.	autograph
4.	faucet	15.	naughty
5.	altogether	16.	ought
6.	brought	17.	retaught
7.	default	18.	awkward
8.	daughter	19.	**Challenge Word**: question
9.	waterfall	20.	**Challenge Word**: already
10.	flawless		**Content Word**: ecology
11.	afterthought		

Student Reader

This week, we are beginning the Reader *Introduction to Ecology*. Your child will learn about the relationships between living things and their environments, food chains, and the forest ecosystem, which includes producers, consumers, and decomposers. Be sure to ask your child each evening about what he or she is learning.

Students will take home text copies of the chapters in the Reader throughout the unit. Encouraging students to read a text directly related to this domain-based unit will provide content and vocabulary reinforcement. Your child will also bring home a copy of the glossary for use in reading the text copies to family members. The bolded words on the text copies are the words found in the glossary.

Living Things and Their Habitats

Ecology is about nature and life. It is about the relationships between living things and their **environment**. Someone who studies **ecology** is an ecologist. An ecologist studies living things and the way they relate to their surroundings.

This toad is part of an **ecosystem**. An **ecosystem** is like a habitat where an **organism** lives, but it includes many habitats plus the nonliving systems that support them. In an **ecosystem**, each living thing **depends on** other living and nonliving things for **survival**. Insects find shelter and food on trees and in moss. The toad finds those insects and eats them. The toad **depends on** rainfall to supply a place to lay eggs. One day, maybe a snake will eat the toad. These are the kinds of things ecologists like to think about!

The bee is attracted to the flower's bright color. The bee eats the flower's sweet nectar. The flower is also full of **pollen**. **Pollen** is a substance that looks like dust. When the bee buzzes off, it carries some of the flower's **pollen** away on its feet and wings.

To make seeds, flowers must share their **pollen** with other flowers. Flowers do not have hands or feet or any other way to get their **pollen** to other flowers. So, they **depend on** bees and other insects to spread it for them. The bee needs the flower in order to **survive**. The flower needs the bee and other insects in order to **survive**. These are perfect examples of the kind of relationships ecologists like to study.

Here is another living thing you probably recognize: a squirrel. She is a little surprised to see you. This squirrel does not see people every day. She is not one of those squirrels you see **skittering** along branches in the park or your backyard. Instead, this squirrel lives deep in the forest.

She has a nest of leaves and sticks somewhere way high up in this tree. In the springtime, the mother squirrel shared her nest with her babies. But now, it is late summer. The babies have left the nest. The mother has the nest to herself. It is time for her to gather food for the winter.

This squirrel's favorite food is acorns, which are nuts from oak trees. In the summer, it is easy for the squirrel to go out and find plenty of acorns. But the squirrel must also gather and save food for winter. In the winter, acorns won't be so easy to find.

The squirrel uses her little paws to dig a hole in the ground. She buries an acorn. Over the summer and early fall, she may bury hundreds of them. Then, whenever she gets hungry during the winter, she can crawl out of her nest and go dig up an acorn.

It is easy to see how the squirrel **depends on** the tree. She uses the tree for both food and shelter. However, the squirrel also gives something to the tree.

How do you think the squirrel remembers where she buried all those acorns? Can she smell them? Does she put a little stick in the ground to mark each acorn? Does she draw a map on the back of a leaf? Actually, she does not remember where she planted all those acorns! She forgets a lot of them. Many of those acorns will remain in the ground right where she buried them.

Acorns are nuts. Nuts are seeds with shells covering them. Like most seeds, acorns need to be planted in order to **sprout** and grow. Well, the squirrel did the oak tree a favor by planting all those acorns and then forgetting about them. If the acorns weren't buried, they probably would not **sprout** and might be eaten by another animal.

The squirrel and the oak tree are each doing what they do to **survive** and produce young. The tree grows leaves and acorns. The squirrel uses the leaves for shelter and the acorns for food. This makes it possible for the squirrel to **survive** and produce young. Also, because the squirrel buries acorns, the oak tree is able to produce young, too. This is how things work in an **ecosystem**. This is what **ecology** is all about!

End-of-Year Silent Reading Assessment

The Cat

Once upon a time in Denmark, there was a man named Franz. Franz lived a good life all year long, until one night. That evening, a pack of horrible, badly-behaved trolls descended on him. The trolls drove poor Franz from his house and took over the place.

This went on for many years on the exact same night every year, until, one year, a famous hunter visited the house the morning of the dreaded night. The hunter had just captured a large, white bear and planned to present it to the King of Denmark. The hunter had a long journey ahead of him and asked Franz if he and the bear could spend the night.

"I would let you stay," said Franz, "but I can't, for every year at this time I am visited by trolls at night who drive me out of the house. They will be here tonight and you do not want to be here when they arrive!"

"Oh," said the hunter, "I am not afraid of trolls. If that is all you are worried about, let me stay in the house. The bear can sleep under the stove there. I will sleep in the back, in the comfortable bedroom."

"Very well," said Franz. "You may stay, at your own risk, but I must get the house ready for the trolls. If I don't, they will be furious."

Franz worked diligently to get his house ready for the trolls. He chopped wood and built a fire. He set the table with his best dishes and loaded them with porridge, assorted fruit, smoked fish, and delicious sausages. When he was done, he left the hunter and the bear in the house and went to stay with a friend.

At sunset, the trolls arrived. They stormed into the house and began a raucous celebration. They ate and drank, sang songs, and made a terrible mess.

One of the trolls caught a glimpse of the bear. It was lying under the stove, with only an ear sticking out.

"Look!" the troll said, "Franz has a cat!"

The troll cut off a bit of sausage and tossed it on the floor. Then, he kicked the bear in the ear and shouted, "Wake up, kitty! Get the sausage!"

The bear rose up on its hind legs, ripping the stove away from the floor. The stove was launched across the room. The bear, in a great fury, roared ferociously. The trolls were terrified. They screamed and ran for their lives.

Franz returned home the next day. He cleaned up the horrific mess the trolls had made, repaired the stove, and lived another year in his house. When the dreaded evening arrived once again the next year, he expected the trolls to come again. He went out into the yard to cut wood for them.

After a few minutes, he heard a voice calling, "Franz! Franz!"

Franz squinted into the woods but saw nothing but trees.

Then, he heard the voice again say, "Franz! Franz!"

"Yes?" Franz said. "What is it?"

"Have you still got that huge, ferocious cat?" the voice asked.

Franz thought for a minute. Then, he replied.

"Yes," Franz said. "I still have the cat. It is lying under the stove, and, earlier this year, it had seven kittens. Now, all of the kittens have grown up. They are bigger and fiercer than their mother!"

"Egad!" said the voice. "Then, you will never see us again!"

Franz heard a rustling of feet in the woods. Then, there was silence.

After that, Franz went on with his life and the trolls never bothered him again.

1. Why did the author write this selection?

    A.   to tell the reader how kind trolls are

    B.   to tell the reader that cats are ferocious

    C.   to tell the reader that using your wits can make for a happy ending

    D.   to tell the reader that people from Denmark are clever

2. What is the meaning of the word **ferocious** in the following sentence

"Have you still got that huge, **ferocious** cat?"

    A.   hungry

    B.   dangerous

    C.   enormous

    D.   furry

3. Using the numbers 1–5, put the following events in order as they occurred in the selection.

_____ Franz told the voices in the forest that his cat had seven kittens.

_____ On the exact same night each year, trolls drove Franz from his house and took over the place.

_____ A troll threw a piece of sausage to the cat lying under the stove.

_____ A hunter asked if he could stay at Franz's house on his way to take the bear he had captured to the King of Denmark.

_____ The bear roared ferociously and scared the trolls away.

4. What is the meaning of the word **<u>raucous</u>** in the following sentence?

> They stormed into the house and began a **<u>raucous</u>** celebration.

    A.   soft

    B.   friendly

    C.   loud

    D.   unfriendly

5. Which of the following describes an event that takes place in the story?

    A.   A troll feeds a bear because he likes bears.

    B.   A cat feeds a troll because the troll is hungry.

    C.   A troll feeds a bear because he thinks it is a cat.

    D.   A troll feeds a cat because he thinks it is a bear.

6. Why did the trolls leave and never return?

_____

_____

_____

7. Write a summary of this selection.

_____

_____

_____

8. What is the meaning of the word **horrific** in the following sentence?

He cleaned up the **horrific** mess the trolls had made.

    A.   huge

    B.   shocking

    C.   orderly

    D.   silly

9. At the end of the story, Franz talked to some creatures that were hiding in the woods. Who do you think these creatures were?

_____

10. Why did Franz tell the mysterious creatures that his cat had seven kittens?

_____

_____

_____

The Wolf, the Elk, and the Aspen Tree

The wolf is the villain in some of the greatest stories ever told.

Who chased the three little pigs and blew down their houses? It was the wolf, of course!

Who pestered Little Red Riding Hood and her grandmother? The wolf!

These are fiction stories, but they tell us a lot about how real people felt about wolves in the old days. For many years, people were scared of wolves. They worried that wolves might attack their farm animals. They also worried that wolves might attack them or their children.

People hated wolves. They disliked them so much that they paid people to hunt them. In England, King William I paid hunters per wolf pelt. The rulers of Russia, the tsars, paid hunters for an adult wolf and half of the adult wolf amount for a wolf cub. The kings of Sweden viewed wolf hunting as a civic duty. They expected every able-bodied man to help out with wolf hunts.

The European settlers who came to America brought this way of thinking with them. They hunted wolves to protect themselves and their livestock. The development of guns helped them. It allowed them to kill more wolves than ever before. By 1920, wolves had been wiped out in most parts of the United States. At the time, almost everyone thought this was a good thing. Most people did not see any reason to keep wolves around. "Good riddance!" they said.

In the past few years, a lot of people have changed their mind about wolves. Scientists who studied Yellowstone National Park were some of the first to change. They noticed that certain kinds of trees were starting to die out in the park. One of the trees they were worried about was the aspen tree. There were lots of old-growth aspen trees in Yellowstone, meaning there were lots of aspen trees that had been there a long time. But there were very few young aspens.

Scientists investigated this. They found that elk were a big part of the problem. Elk like the taste of aspen seedlings and there were lots of elk in the park. In the old days, packs of wolves preyed on the elk. The wolves kept the herds of elk from getting too big. But the wolves had been wiped out. There were no predators left who hunted for elk. A pack of elk could spend all day eating aspen seedlings. They did not have to worry about predators.

The scientists had an idea. They thought they might be able to help the aspen trees by bringing in wolves. This idea was very controversial. Many farmers and ranchers objected. They still viewed the wolves as farmers in the old days had—as a threat to people and livestock. They thought bringing wolves back was a bad idea.

It took many years to convince people that it might be a good idea to bring wolves to Yellowstone. Wolves were finally re-introduced there in 1995.

Several years later the scientists went back to the park to see of their plan was working. They found evidence that it was. Many of the wolves they had brought in survived. The wolves had formed packs and begun hunting. They were also having pups. There were still lots of elk in the park, but the elk were starting to get nervous. They could no longer spend all day nibbling aspen saplings, without a care in the world. They had to be a bit more careful. Some aspen trees had survived. They had grown large enough that elk could no longer eat them.

"This is really exciting!" said one of the researchers. "It's great news for Yellowstone. The level of recovery we are seeing is very encouraging."

So here is one story in which the wolf is not the villain!

There are some lessons for human beings in this story. One lesson is that we need to be careful when we make decisions about the value of a species. In the past, we decided that some animals are just plain bad. We decided that the planet would be better without these animals. In the past few decades we have come to understand that it is dangerous to think that way. All of the animals and plants in an ecosystem are interdependent. That means they all depend on each other. They are connected in ways we may not notice at first. When we get rid of one animal, we may put other animals or plants at risk. We may remove an animal's food source or we may remove its main predator, as happened in Yellowstone. Every ecosystem has its own balance. If we remove one species, we may throw the whole system out of balance.

11. Why is the wolf seen as good in this selection?

_____

_____

12. Why was the scientists' idea about bringing in wolves controversial?

_____

_____

13. Choose the food chain found in Yellowstone National Park that is described in the selection.

    A.   Aspen tree → Elk →Wolf

    B.   Elk → Aspen tree →Wolf

    C.   Wolf → Aspen tree →Elk

    D.   Wolf →Elk →Aspen Tree

14. Why did the author write this selection?

    A.   to inform readers about how the wolf helped in Yellowstone

    B.   to warn readers about wild animals when visiting Yellowstone

    C.   to entertain readers with a story about a wolf, an elk, and an aspen tree

    D.   to describe the author's visit to Yellowstone on vacation

15. What evidence did scientists find that their plan was working?

_____

_____

16. What does **civic duty** mean in the following sentence from the selection?

> The kings of Sweden viewed wolf hunting as a **civic duty**. They expected every able-bodied man to help out with wolf hunts.

    A.   a responsibility that citizens are expected to avoid

    B.   an act that citizens should try once in their life

    C.   a responsibility that citizens are expected to take part in

    D.   an act that people must do in order to become citizens

17. What could have happened if the scientists had not put their plan in place?

_____

_____

18. What is the main idea of this selection?

_____

_____

19. Why did most European settlers dislike wolves so much?

    A.   Wolves were kept as pets in Europe.

    B.   People were scared of wolves.

    C.   The wolf population grew too fast.

    D.   Europeans brought wolves with them for trading.

20. Why did elk have to be a bit more careful once the scientists' plan was in place?

_____

_____

Invasive Species

In today's world, people are on the move. Salesmen jet from one city to another. Tourists visit foreign countries. Immigrants leave their homes and settle in new lands.

But did you know that animals are also on the move? Sometimes people bring exotic animals back from their trips. Sometimes, they buy exotic animals in pet shops. Other times, the animals travel by themselves. They may sneak into crates that are shipped from one country to another or they may find their way onto ships that cross the oceans.

This animal travel has caused some problems. Sometimes animals end up in a new place which is just right for them. The land is just right for them. The climate is perfect. There is lots of food. This is a good thing for them. But it may be a bad thing for other animals in the ecosystem. The newly arrived animals may settle in and have babies. They may disrupt the ecosystem by eating up or crowding out the native animals. When this happens, we say the ecosystem has a problem with "invasive species." The ecosystem is being invaded by outsiders.

There are invasive species in many parts of the United States. In Florida, the invasive species that people are most worried about these days is the Burmese python. Burmese pythons are snakes that are native to Asia. They are big snakes. An average Burmese python is twelve feet long.

Burmese pythons like to live near water, but they can also slither up into trees. These snakes are carnivores. They eat small mammals like rats and mice. They also eat birds. The Burmese python is a constrictor. It bites its victim and holds it. Then, it wraps itself around the victim and squeezes it to death. Once the victim is dead, the snake swallows it whole.

So how did these Burmese pythons make their way to Florida? Some people like to keep snakes as pets. For a long time, you could buy a Burmese python for about twenty dollars. You could feed it mice and watch it grow. There was only one problem: the snake might eventually get too big for its cage. Experts think some pet owners set their snakes free when they got too big. Some pythons may also have escaped when a hurricane hit Florida in 1996.

In any case, thousands of Burmese pythons now make their home in the swamps of southern Florida. This part of Florida is warm, wet, and full of small mammals. At least, it used to be full of small mammals. A 2011 study found that lots of small mammals in these areas are in trouble. The pythons are gobbling up raccoons, rabbits, and opossums. They are even eating larger animals, including deer, bobcats, and alligators!

Experts are worried. They are afraid that the pythons may wipe out some of the endangered species that live in the area. A new law has made it illegal for pet shops in the United States to sell Burmese pythons. Another law has allowed hunters to hunt pythons. Officials are hoping these laws will help keep the python problem under control.

In the Midwest, people are worried about Asian carp. Asian carp are fish that are native to Asia. Some of them were brought to the United States in the 1970s. They got loose in the Mississippi River. Now, they are spreading like wildfire. The carp are not just in the Mississippi River. They have also been found in other rivers that feed into the Mississippi. People are worried that they may get into the Great Lakes.

Asian carp are big eaters. They gobble up food that other fish need. The carp get so big that other fish can't eat them. So, the arrival of Asian carp is bad news for other fish.

Asian carp are dangerous in another way, too. They are amazing jumpers. An Asian carp can jump eight to ten feet in the air.

Asian carp tend to be scared by boats. If you drive a motorboat past them, they may start to jump out of the water. You may see hundreds of flying fish. You may even be hit with a fish. A number of people have been injured by these jumping fish.

Invasive species, like the Burmese python and Asian carp, can harm environments they invade. Animals and plants suffer and some of the damage caused by these invasive species may be permanent.

21. What does the word **exotic** mean in the following sentence from the selection?

> Sometimes people bring **exotic** animals back from their trips.

    A.   tame

    B.   intended as a pet in the home

    C.   not living or growing naturally in a certain area

    D.   not found in nature

22. How did Burmese pythons come to make their home in the swamps of southern Florida?

_____

_____

_____

23. What might happen if Asian carp get into the Great Lakes?

_____

_____

24. List the ways that animals are on the move according to the selection.

1. _____

2. _____

3. _____

25. Circle the correct answer to fill in the blank in the following sentence:

> Invasive species disrupt the _____ by eating up or crowding out the native animals.

    carnivores   wildfire   ecosystem   travelers

26. How are Asian carp dangerous to humans?

_____

_____

_____

27. Why did the author write this selection?

    A.   to describe the habitat of pythons

    B.   to entertain with a story about animals

    C.   to create panic about visiting Florida and areas near the Mississippi River

    D.   to inform about how invasive species can be harmful

28. How have officials in Florida tried to keep the python problem under control?

_____

_____

29. What does the phrase **spreading like wildfire** mean in the following sentence from the selection?

> They got loose in the Mississippi River. Now, they are **spreading like wildfire**.

    A.   acts or moves quickly and intensely

    B.   slows down so it is almost not noticeable

    C.   moves at a steady pace

    D.   acts as if in shock and stays in one place

30. Write a summary of this selection.

_____

_____

_____

_____

Grade 3 End-of-Year Assessment Summary

Student _____

Date:_____

Teacher _____

Recommended placement for next year (Check one)

_____ Above grade level

_____ On grade level

_____ Slightly below grade level

_____ Needs intensive remediation

*Fill in the information on this sheet and place this sheet in the Reading Folder for next year's teacher. Staple the actual student assessment worksheets to the back of this page.

A. Summary of Missed Letter-Sound Correspondences and Syllabication from Worksheets 3.6 and 3.7 (If administered)

List the missed letter-sound correspondences and syllabication errors in the spaces below:

_____ _____ _____ _____

_____ _____ _____ _____

_____ _____ _____ _____

_____ _____ _____ _____

_____ _____ _____ _____

Other Notes:

Name: _____

B. Fluency

W.C.P.M. Calculation Worksheet

Student: _____ Date:_____

Story: *The Elephant and the Ape*

Total words: 464

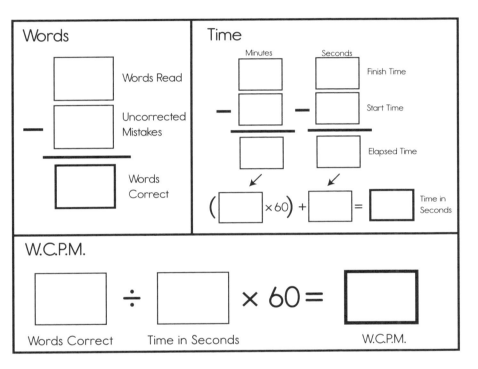

Compare the student's W.C.P.M. score to national norms for Spring of Grade 3 (Hasbrouck and Tindal, 2006):

W.C.P.M	National Percentiles for Spring, Grade 3
162	90th
137	75th
107	50th
78	25th
48	10th

Comprehension Total _____ / 5

Answers Correct	Level
5	Independent comprehension level
4	Instructional comprehension level
2–3	Frustration comprehension level
0–1	Intensive remediation warranted for this student

C. Silent Reading Comprehension

Category of Questions	Score Required to meet Benchmark of 80%	Student Score
Author's Purpose	3/3	____/3
Inference	6/7	____/7
Literal	8/9	____/9
Main Idea	1/1	____/1
Sequencing	2/2	____/2
Summary	2/2	____/2
Words in Context	5/6	____/6

D. Grammar

Category of Questions	Score Required to meet Benchmark of 80%	Student Score
Parts of a paragraph	4/5	____/5
Parts of speech	4/4	____/4
Subject/Predicate	1/1	____/1
Conjunctions	3/3	____/3
Capitalization/ Punctuation	1/1	____/1
Punctuation	1/1	____/1
Verbs	2/2	____/2
Linking Words	4/5	____/5
Possessives	4/4	____/4
Comparative/ Superlative Adjectives	4/4	____/4

E. Morphology

Category of Questions	Score Required to meet Benchmark of 80%	Student Score
Prefixes	12/15	____/15
Suffixes	12/15	____/15

Food Chains

1. What happens to the acorns that aren't eaten by the animals in the forest?

_____

Page _____

2. Create a food chain in which you are the apex predator.

Read the following statements, write *true* or *false*, and write the page number that has the answer.

	True or False	Page Number
A worm is an apex predator.		
There are no hidden creatures in the forest ecosystem.		
Small animals are eaten by slightly larger animals.		
All food chains include plants.		
When a spider's egg sac opens, two tiny spiders emerge.		

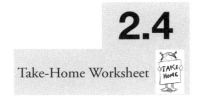

Food Chains

Now you know something about squirrels and oak trees. Each has something to offer the other. The tree may produce thousands of acorns each year, but only a few will actually sprout and become **saplings**. Of those **saplings**, only a couple will survive and grow into **mighty** oaks, spreading their roots and changing with the seasons.

The rest of the acorns will be eaten by one creature or another. Deer eat them sometimes and so do various birds that **wander** through the forest, such as turkeys and woodpeckers. The acorns that aren't eaten will get covered by leaves, soaked by rain, and frozen by snow. If they aren't eaten by worms or other underground things, some of them will sprout into **saplings**.

In the forest ecosystem, living things depend on one another. Many living things depend on trees for shelter and food. You can almost certainly find bugs on any tree. Woodpeckers can find them too!

If you dig down into the soil or scrape away some tree bark, you will discover all sorts of other critters in the forest ecosystem, such as worms, beetles, and ants.

You might not see all those insects and other little critters when you look around the forest, but they are there! You can find them under leaves, rocks, and fallen trees. Mostly, their world is underground and out of sight, unless you are willing to get dirty digging for them!

What are all those bugs doing there? They are doing what all living things do: surviving. To survive, living things need food. The **nutrients** in food provide energy for the body. Without energy, the body stops. It's that simple!

What else are bugs and other living things doing besides eating? They are doing whatever it is they need to do in order to produce young. Plants make seeds. Mammals, such as squirrels and deer, give birth to live babies. Bugs and birds lay eggs.

Spiders make egg sacs like the one in this image. When the sac opens, hundreds of tiny baby spiders will run out. Most of them will be eaten by other bugs. Those that survive will grow to be hunters like their parents.

Living things also must develop ways to **protect** themselves from other things in the ecosystem. Squirrels build their nests high in trees, away from **predators**. Worms dig down into the soil. Snails and turtles have shells to **protect** them.

Unfortunately for squirrels, worms, snails, and turtles, these **defenses** do not always work. The **predators** that hunt and eat other animals for a living have sharp teeth and claws for catching their **prey**.

There are ecosystems in many places. Each ecosystem has its own **food chain**. Look at the image of the wolf, the deer, and the acorn. This is a very simple way to think of the **food chain**. Smaller animals are eaten by slightly larger animals. But this image only represents a small part of a real **food chain**. Most **food chains** also include plants. They also include bacteria and other tiny, **microscopic** organisms.

Plants and smaller animals are usually near the bottom of the **food chain**. At the top of the **food chain**, you will find beasts like grizzly bears, lions, blue whales, or great white sharks. These animals are too big to be hunted by anything else. A lion or shark is called an **apex predator** because it is at the top of the **food chain**

End-of Year Grammar Assessment

Read the following paragraph carefully and then answer questions 1–4.

> Summer is the very best time of year! Our family always goes to the beach and we play in the sand and surf for days. We love to build sandcastles and watch the waves creep in and flatten them. The next day we just build them again. If we're lucky we will see the dolphins swimming offshore. Tulips bloom in the spring. I can't wait for summer to arrive so we can head toward the ocean again!

1. Which of the following is the topic sentence of the paragraph?

   A. Our family always goes to the beach and we play in the sand and surf for days.

   B. Tulips bloom in the spring.

   C. I can't wait for summer to arrive so we can head toward the ocean again!

   D. Summer is the very best time of year!

2. Which of the following is the concluding sentence of the paragraph?

   A. Our family always goes to the beach and we play in the sand and surf for days.

   B. Tulips bloom in the spring.

   C. I can't wait for summer to arrive so we can head toward the ocean again!

   D. Summer is the very best time of year!

3. Which of the following is an irrelevant sentence in the paragraph?

    A.   Our family always goes to the beach and we play in the sand and surf for days.

    B.   Tulips bloom in the spring.

    C.   I can't wait for summer to arrive so we can head toward the ocean again!

    D.   Summer is the very best time of year!

4. Which of the following would be the best title for the paragraph?

    A.   Tulips are Beautiful

    B.   Summer Fun

    C.   Summer, Fall, Winter, and Spring

    D.   Dolphins Swim in the Surf

5. Number the following sentences in order as they should appear in a paragraph about making scrambled eggs:

    _____ Mix the eggs with a splash of milk and a dash of salt and pepper.

    _____ Get the eggs out of the refrigerator.

    _____ Enjoy your warm scrambled eggs with toast and jam!

    _____ Cook the eggs over a low heat so they don't burn.

Read the following sentences carefully and then answer questions 6–9.

The weekly basketball game excited and thrilled all of us greatly.

The two teams played enthusiastically in the large gym at Scottsdale Elementary School.

We arrived early to get the best seats and stayed until the final, climactic seconds.

---

6. Choose the answer with words that are nouns.

    A.   played, gym, early

    B.   game, seats, seconds

    C.   game, excited, gets

    D.   thrilled, gym, final

7. Choose the answer with words that are verbs.

    A.   thrilled, arrived, stayed

    B.   excited, early, best

    C.   thrilled, greatly, final

    D.   excited, gym, get

8. Choose the answer with words that are adjectives.

    A.   thrilled, large, best

    B.   game, early, final

    C.   large, best, climactic

    D.   all, large, until

9. Choose the answer with words that are adverbs.

    A.   excited, early, climactic

    B.   Elementary, early, stayed

    C.   greatly, enthusiastically, early

    D.   Scottsville, best, final

10. Draw a vertical line to separate subject and predicate in the following sentence.

The striped hot air balloon drifted high in the puffy clouds.

11. Which sentence uses the conjunction **but** correctly?

    A.   Mrs. Wells said we could have both recess but extra time to read after the spelling test.

    B.   The child's picture was painted green, purple, but yellow.

    C.   Bob likes to read nonfiction, but Bill would rather read fiction.

    D.   The babysitter said, "You may stay up until 9:00 tonight but you finished your supper!"

12. Choose the sentence that uses the conjunction **because** correctly.

    A.   Because we left the picnic early the thunderstorm drenched everyone's lunch.

    B.   Mom is baking a three layer birthday cake because Dad turns 30 years old today.

    C.   Because we spelled all of our spelling words correctly we practiced the words carefully.

    D.   We blew out all the candles in the room because it got very dark.

13. Which sentence uses the conjunction **so** correctly?

    A.   My sister knocked over her glass of milk so she helped clean it up.

    B.   We watched television inside so the storm came up suddenly.

    C.   My friend was very excited so he won the game.

    D.   We arrived at the movie on time so we left the house early.

14. Write the sentence using correct capitalization and punctuation.

> your disguise is so creative that I hardly recognized you said Donny

_____

_____

15. Write the sentence adding commas where needed.

> Mary invited Fran Molly and Nancy to her house for an afternoon of movies and popcorn.

_____

_____

16. Circle the letter of the sentence that uses the past tense of the verb correctly.

   A.   Reggie eats more ice cream than all of his brothers.

   B.   The threatening clouds will scare away the children.

   C.   My trip to the ocean last weekend calmed and renewed my spirit.

   D.   The department store is having a half price sale.

17. Write the correct verb on the blank.

   The fussy baby will _____ lots of attention from her grandparents.
                        (have, has)

18. Choose the sentence that uses the linking words **_for example_** correctly.

    A.   The girl loves to cook, for example, for her family grilled cheese sandwiches, tomato soup, and apple pie.

    B.   Lamps come in all shapes and sizes, for example, table lamps, floor lamps, and hanging lamps.

    C.   The shopper finds wonderful bargains at the store, for example.

    D.   Birds fly overhead, for example, singing their songs, moving from place to place and looking for food.

19. Choose the sentence that is true.

    A.   To compare two things and to contrast two things is the same activity.

    B.   Comparing means to find what is different among things.

    C.   Contrasting means to find what is the same among things.

    D.   To compare two things and to contrast two things are opposite activities.

20. Which sentence uses the linking words **_in the same way_** correctly?

    A.   We live on a farm in the country. In the same way, you live in downtown New York City.

    B.   The third grade class is on a field trip today. In the same way, the fourth grade class is on a trip, too.

    C.   Hannah is a very pleasant person. In the same way, Hank is a mean person.

    D.   Wanda grew three inches last year. In the same way, her brother has been the same height for years.

21. The words *in conclusion* signal _____.

    A.   two things are the same.

    B.   a summary is coming up next.

    C.   two things are different.

    D.   a cause and effect are coming up next.

22. Choose the sentence that uses the words *in contrast* correctly.

    A.   The clowns make us laugh. In contrast, the funny movie makes us laugh, too.

    B.   Fairy tale giants are make-believe. In contrast, flying elephants are found in fiction.

    C.   The desks in our classroom are all lined up. In contrast, the desks across the hall are all out of order.

    D.   Spelling is an easy subject for me. In contrast, grammar isn't difficult either.

23. Write the correct singular possessive noun on the blank.

We are all invited to _____ house for a party.
               (the house of our teacher)

24. Which sentence uses the apostrophe correctly?

    A.   The freshly baked cookies' were delicious.

    B.   The cookie frosting's was gooey and yummy.

    C.   Chocolate chip and peanut butter cookie's are my favorite!

    D.   Can you see all of the cookies' burned edges?

25. Choose the sentence that is correct.

      A.   Lions, tigers, and bears are coming this way!

      B.   The lions roars could be heard all over the zoo.

      C.   The stripes on the tigers fur are orange and yellow.

      D.   Do you see the bears claws scratching the tree?

26. Write the correct possessive pronoun on the blank.

Can the rushing river overflow _____ banks?

(its, it's)

Write the correct form of the comparative or superlative adjective or adverb in the blank.

27. (thin) The apple slices on your plate are cut in _____ slices than the apple slices on my plate.

28. (unusual) The paintings in that museum are the _____ I've ever seen!

29. (close) Our grandmother lives _____ to the mall than we do.

30. (correctly) Our class recited multiplication tables _____ than the other class.

Name: _____

Anticipation Guide for
"Producers, Consumers, and Decomposers"

| Before Reading | | Statement | After Reading | | |
True	False		True	False	Page
		Dirt is just a yucky mess.			
		A blackberry plant is a producer.			
		Consumers make their own food.			
		Earthworms are decomposers.			
		Bacteria are the most important decomposers.			

1. What would happen to the forest ecosystem if all of the bacteria disappeared?

_____

_____

_____

2. Match the definition to the word by writing the letter on the blank.

_____ Producer   A. eats other plants or animals

_____ Consumer   B. breaks down bodies into simpler and simpler matter

_____ Decomposer   C. makes food

3. What is this chapter mostly about?

    A.   Squirrels are afraid of owls.

    B.   Blackberry jam is the best.

    C.   All living things can be sorted into three categories.

    D.   Wild animals such as bears, birds, and bugs eat berries.

Prefix Review

Complete each sentence by adding the correct prefix to the root word.

mid–	tri–	multi–	over–	bi–	under–	uni–

1. Thomas is slowly learning how to ride his new _____ cycle with the extra training wheels and is almost ready to rely on just two wheels.

2. Over the years, people have _____ fished one river outside of the small mountain town, which now has almost no fish in it as a result.

3. The _____ powered fans cooled us off very quickly because they blew so much air on us.

4. We learned the names of special types of _____ angles in math and the names are based on angles on the inside of the figures.

5. There is a big assessment in my history class at _____ term to determine what we have learned in the first half of the year.

6. The principal of the school asked if we liked the new _____ color uniforms better than the old ones.

7. During the _____ media presentation, the teacher used videos and music to show how people in different countries celebrate holidays.

8. The _____ monthly meeting of the book club occurs on a Tuesday at the library and is open to anyone who has read the book for that meeting.

9. The team captains met with the referees at _____ field to determine which side of the field each team would start on and who would get the ball first.

10. The cable company _____ charged us on this month's bill for features we don't have and Dad had to call and fix the problem so the charge would be the normal amount.

Write a sentence using each word.

1. *unison*

_____

_____

2. *underground*

_____

_____

3. *overeat*

_____

_____

Blank Busters

author	dawdle	altogether	default
waterfall	afterthought	caution	naughty
squawked	faucet	brought	daughter
flawless	already	ought	awkward
autograph	retaught		

Challenge Word: question
Challenge Word: always
Content Word: ecology

Fill in the blanks in the sentences below with one of the spelling words in the chart. Only if needed, add a suffix to the end of a word in order for the sentence to make sense: *–s*, *–ed*, *–ing*, *–er*, or *–ly*.

1.   Before railroad crossings, there are usually _____ signals to let you know when a train is approaching.

2.   By November, squirrels have _____ buried enough acorns to last through the winter.

3.   Celia's sister received an _____ picture of the band.

4.   She passed the basketball _____ because this was her first practice.

5.   The families went to the mountains and saw beautiful _____ on their way to the picnic area.

6. I reminded my twin _____ that they _____ to study for their spelling assessment on Friday.

7. The _____ of the mystery series came to speak at our school.

8. All of our _____ are leaking so the plumber is coming to fix them this afternoon.

9. There were _____ seven faucets that needed adjustments.

10. The class eagerly waited for the lesson on _____ to learn how they can improve our environment.

Write three sentences using spelling words of your choice that were not used in the first ten sentences. Make sure to use correct capitalization and punctuation. You may use the Challenge Words or Content Word in your sentences.

1. _____

_____

2. _____

_____

3. _____

_____

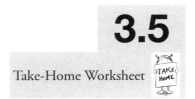

Producers, Consumers, and Decomposers

Do you recognize the brown material in this picture? Some people call it dirt.

Dirt is what you are supposed to wipe off your shoes and wash off your hands, right? Dirt is what you are never supposed to get on your good shirt, right? To some people, dirt is just yucky and needs to be cleaned up.

Well, ecologists don't mind getting dirty. Ecologists know dirt is very important. In fact, ecologists don't call it dirt at all. They call it **soil**. Without **soil**, life on land as we know it could not exist. **Soil** is at the heart of most ecosystems on land.

In the forest ecosystem, every living thing can be sorted into one of three basic categories: **producers**, **consumers**, and **decomposer**s.

Producers make their own food. Plants do this through the process of **photosynthesis**. Many **producers** also happen to produce, or make, things that animals eat. The blackberry plant is a tasty example. It makes its own food through **photosynthesis**. The berries contain the plant's seeds. Wild animals such as birds, bears, and bugs eat the berries. The animals eat the juicy berries, but they do not digest the tiny seeds.

Consumers eat other plants and animals. As you can probably guess, squirrels are acorn **consumers**. Unfortunately for squirrels, they are not at the top of the food chain.

This owl is a skilled predator. It is nocturnal, meaning it hunts at night. It consumes small rodents, including squirrels. With excellent hearing and eyesight, the owl will catch any squirrel or other rodent who leaves the **safety** of its nest at night.

Decomposers are the third type of living thing in the forest ecosystem. Earthworms are **decomposers**. They feed on dead **organic** matter, such as leaves. The worms pull the leaves down into the ground. They shred the leaves into little pieces and then eat them.

Worms are pretty low on the food chain. Fish, birds, frogs, and turtles will all eat any worm unlucky enough to cross their paths.

Some insects are pretty big. Some are so small you need a magnifying glass to see them. Some fly. Some crawl.

Some insects are **decomposers**. Others are **consumers** and some are even predators. Most insects are pretty far down on the food chain.

In fact, there are billions and billions of other living things in the **soil** surrounding the worm. These **bacteria**, **fungi**, and other organisms are working to survive in the same **soil**. These organisms are so small you cannot see them without a microscope.

Bacteria are the most important **decomposers**. They are also the most **abundant** form of life in an ecosystem. **Bacteria** and other simple organisms have a very, very important job.

Bacteria and other teeny, tiny organisms cause dead plant and animal matter to **decompose**. When something **decomposes**, its body is broken down into simpler and simpler types of matter.

As leaves **decompose**, their nutrients will become part of the **soil**. Basically, the **decomposed** matter provides **vitamins** and **minerals** for new plants or other living things.

Word Reading in Isolation Assessment

1.	steady	asphalt	oxygen	dovetail	birthplace
2.	bravo	washtub	consume	delight	council
3.	accuse	riddle	trolley	scoreboard	cruise
4.	marvelous	betrayal	freighter	floored	guarantee
5.	blizzard	prairie	concrete	crescent	bowlful
6.	breakwater	peachy	spiffier	gherkin	qualify
7.	yearning	exercise	loathe	ivory	disprove
8.	audit	baboon	continue	taught	overdue
9.	chasm	human	pulled	warning	worthless
10.	scowl	avoidance	paperboy	courses	woodchuck
11.	switch	crumb	whopper	sprinkle	knitting
12.	calculate	mustache	partridge	singe	assign
13.	wriggle	bizarre	recommit	youthful	mistletoe

Word Reading in Isolation Scoring Sheet

Word Reading in Isolation Scoring Sheet

	a	b	c	d	e
1	steady	asphalt	oxygen	dovetail	birthplace
	/s/ /t/ /e/ /d/ • /ee/	/a/ /s/ • /f/ /aw/ /l/ /t/	/o/ /x/ • /i/ /j/•/ə/ /n/	/d/ /u/ /v/ • /t/ /ae/ /l/	/b/ /er/ /th/ • /p/ /l/ /ae/ /s/
	closed • open	closed • digraph	closed • closed • ə	digraph • digraph	r-controlled • digraph
2	bravo	washtub	consume	delight	council
	/b/ /r/ /o/ /v/ • /oe/	/w/ /aw/ /sh/ • /t/ /u/ /b/	/k/ /u/ /n/ • /s/ /oo/ /m/	/d/ /ə/ • /l/ /ie/ /t/	/k/ /ou/ /n/ • /s/ /ə/ /l/
	closed • open	closed • closed	closed • digraph	ə • digraph	digraph • ə
3	accuse	riddle	trolley	scoreboard	cruise
	/ə/ /k/ • /k/ /ue/ /z/	/r/ /i/ /d/ • /d/ /ə/ /l/	/t/ /r/ /o/ /l/ • /l/ /ee/	/s/ /k/ /or/ • /b/ /or/ /d/	/k/ /r/ /oo/ /z/
	ə • digraph	closed • – le	closed • open	r-controlled • r-controlled	
4	marvelous	betrayal	freighter	floored	guarantee
	/m/ /ar/ • /v/ /ə/ /l/ • /u/ /s/	/b/ /ə/ • /t/ /r/ /ae/ • /ə/ /l/	/f/ /r/ /ae/ /t/ • /er/	/f/ /l/ /or/ /d/	/g/ /air/ • /ə/ /n/ • /t/ /ee/
	r-cont. • closed • digraph	ə • digraph • ə	digraph • r-controlled		r-cont. • closed • open
5	blizzard	prairie	concrete	crescent	bowlful
	/b/ /l/ /i/ /z/ • /z/ /er/ /d/	/p/ /r/ /air/ • /ee/	/k/ /o/ /n/ • /k/ /r/ /ee/ /t/	/k/ /r/ /e/ /s/ • /e/ /n/ /t/	/b/ /oe/ /l/ • /f/ /ə/ /l/
	closed • r-controlled	r-controlled • open	closed • digraph	closed • closed	
6	breakwater	peachy	spiffier	gherkin	qualify
	/b/ /r/ /ae/ /k/ • /w/ /o/ /t/ • /er/	/p/ /ee/ /ch/ • /ee/	/s/ /p/ /i/ /f/ • /f/ /ee/ • /er/	/g/ /er/ • /k/ /i/ /n/	/k/ /w/ /o/ /l/ • /i/ /f/ • /ie/
	digraph • closed • r-controlled	digraph • open	closed • open • r-cont.	r-controlled • closed	closed • closed • open
7	yearning	exercise	loathe	ivory	disprove
	/y/ /er/ /n/ • /i/ /ng/	/e/ /x/ • /er/ • /s/ /ie/ /z/	/l/ /oe/ /th/	/ie/ • /v/ /or/ • /ee/	/d/ /i/ /s/ • /p/ /r/ /oo/ /v/
	r-controlled • closed	closed • r-cont. • digraph		open • r-cont. • open	closed • digraph

#					
8	audit /aw/ • /d/ /i/ /t/ digraph • closed	baboon /b/ /a/ /b/ • /oo/ /n/ closed • digraph	continue /k/ /u/ /n/ • /t/ /i/ /n/ • /ue/ closed • closed • open	taught /t/ /aw/ /t/	overdue /oe/ • /v/ /er/ • /d/ /oo/ open • r-cont. • digraph
9	chasm /k/ /a/ /z/ • /ə/ /m/ closed • ə	human /h/ /ue/ • /m/ /ə/ /n/ open • ə	pulled /p/ /oo/ /l/ /d/	warning /w/ /or/ /n/ • /i/ /ng/ r-controlled • closed	worthless /w/ /er/ /th/ • /l/ /e/ /s/ r-controlled • closed
10	scowl /s/ /k/ /ou/ /l/	avoidance /ə/ • /v/ /oi/ /d/ • /ə/ /n/ /s/ ə • digraph • ə	paperboy /p/ /ae/ • /p/ /er/ • /b/ /oi/ open • r-cont. • digraph	courses /k/ /or/ /s/ • /e/ /z/ r-controlled • closed	woodchuck /w/ /oo/ /d/ • /ch/ /u/ /k/ digraph • closed
11	switch /s/ /w/ /i/ /ch/	crumb /k/ /r/ /u/ /m/	whopper /w/ /o/ /p/ • /p/ /er/ closed • r-controlled	sprinkle /s/ /p/ /r/ /i/ /ng/ • /k/ /ə/ /l/ closed • -le	knitting /n/ /i/ /t/ • /i/ /ng/ closed • closed
12	calculate /k/ /a/ /l/ • /k/ /ue/ • /l/ /ae/ /t/ closed • open • digraph	mustache /m/ /u/ /s/ • /t/ /a/ /sh/ closed • closed	partridge /p/ • /t/ /r/ /i/ /j/ /ar/ r-controlled • closed	singe /s/ /i/ /n/ /j/	assign /ə/ • /s/ • /s/ /ie/ /n/ ə • digraph
13	wriggle /r/ /i/ /g/ • /g/ /ə/ /l/ closed • -le	bizarre /b/ /i/ /z/ • /z/ /ar/ closed • r-controlled	recommit /r/ /ee/ • /k/ /u/ /m/ • /m/ /i/ /t/ open • closed • closed	youthful /y/ /oo/ /th/ • /f/ /ə/ /l/ digraph • ə	mistletoe /m/ /i/ /s/ • /ə/ /l/ • /t/ /oe/ closed • -le • open

Word Reading in Isolation Analysis

After scoring the assessment, you might find it helpful to determine which phonemes students missed that caused them to score below the benchmark for word recognition. Note that one-syllable words are not included on the Syllabication Analysis.

Score required to meet benchmark of 80%	
Phonemes	
Consonants /b/ /d/ /f/ /g/ /h/ /j/ /k/ /l/ /m/ /n/ /p/ /r/ /s/ /t/ /v/ /w/ /x/ /y/ /z/ /ch/ /sh/ /th/ /th/ /ng/	164/204
Vowels (totals)	107/133
/a/ /e/ /i/ /o/ /u/	36/46
/ae/ /ee/ /ie/ /oe/ /ue/	24/30
/ə/ /oo/ /oo/ /aw/ /ou/	21/26
/oi/ /ar/ /er/ /or/ /air/ /ə/+/l/	25/31
Syllabication (words with 2 or more syllables)	
Closed Syllable/short	38/47
Open Syllable/long	13/16
Magic E and Digraph Syllable	20/25
R-Controlled Syllable	19/21
ə Syllable	9/11
– le Syllable	4/4

The following sheets are provided for your use in directing remediation.

Write the names of students who missed questions under each header. This will help you determine what kind of remediation is needed.

Refer to the Table of Contents in the *Assessment and Remediation Guide* to locate information about specific phonemes and syllabication for remediation purposes.

Word Reading in Isolation Remediation Guide

Phonemes — Consonants

/b/ (1e, 2a, 2b, 3d, 4b, 5a, 5e, 6a, 8b, 10c, 13b)	/d/ (1a, 1d, 2d, 3b, 3d, 4d, 5a, 7e, 8a, 8e, 9c, 10b, 10e)	/f/ (1b, 4c, 4d, 5e, 6c, 6e, 13d)
/g/ (4e, 6d, 13a)	/h/ (9b)	/j/ (1c, 12c, 12d)
/k/ (2c, 2e, 3a, 3d, 3e, 5c, 5d, 6a, 6d, 6e, 8c, 9a, 10a, 10d, 10e, 11b, 11d, 12a, 13c)	/l/ (1b, 1d, 1e, 2d, 2e, 3c, 4a, 4d, 5a, 5e, 6e, 7c, 9c, 9e, 10a, 12a)	/m/ (2c, 4a, 9a, 9b, 11b, 12b, 13c, 13e)
/n/ (1c, 2c, 2e, 4e, 5c, 5d, 6d, 7a, 8b, 8c, 9b, 9d, 10b, 11e, 12d, 12e)	/p/ (1e, 5b, 6b, 6c, 7e, 9c, 10c, 11c, 11d, 12c)	/r/ (2a, 3b, 3c, 3e, 4b, 4c, 5b, 5c, 5d, 6a, 7e, 11b, 11d, 12c, 13a, 13c)
/s/ (1a, 1b, 1e, 2c, 2e, 3d, 4a, 5d, 6c, 7b, 7e, 9e, 10a, 10b, 10d, 11a, 11d, 12b, 12d, 12e, 13e)	/t/ (1a, 1b, 1d, 2b, 2d, 3c, 4b, 4c, 4e, 5c, 5d, 6a, 8a, 8c, 8d, 11e, 12a, 12b, 12c, 13c, 13e)	/v/ (1d, 2a, 4a, 7d, 7e, 8e, 10b)

/w/ (2b, 6a, 6e, 9d, 9e, 10e, 11a, 11c)	/x/ (1c, 7b)	/y/ (7a, 13d)
_____	_____	_____
_____	_____	_____
_____	_____	_____
/z/ (3a, 3e, 5a, 7b, 9a, 10d, 13b)	/ch/ (6b, 10e, 11a)	/sh/ (2b, 12b)
_____	_____	_____
_____	_____	_____
_____	_____	_____
/th/ (1e, 9e, 13d)	/th/ (7c)	/ng/ (7a, 9d, 11d, 11e)
_____	_____	_____
_____	_____	_____
_____	_____	_____

Phonemes —Vowels

/a/ (1b, 8b, 9a, 12a, 12b)	/e/ (1a, 5d, 7b, 9e, 10d	/i/ (1c, 3b, 5a, 6c, 6d, 6e, 7a, 7e, 8a, 8c, 9d, 11a, 11d, 11e, 12c, 12d, 13a, 13b, 13c, 13e)
_____	_____	_____
_____	_____	_____
_____	_____	_____
/o/ (1c, 2a, 3c, 5c, 6a, 6e, 11c)	/u/ (1d, 2b, 2c, 4a, 8c, 10e, 11b, 12b, 13c)	/ae/ (1d, 1e, 4b, 4c, 6a, 10c, 12a)
_____	_____	_____
_____	_____	_____
_____	_____	_____
/ee/ (1a, 3c, 4e, 5b, 5c, 6b, 6c, 7d, 13c)	/ie/ (2d, 6e, 7b, 7d, 12e)	/oe/ (2a, 5e, 7c, 8e, 13e)
_____	_____	_____
_____	_____	_____
_____	_____	_____
/ue/ (3a, 8c, 9b, 12a)	/ə/ (1c, 2d, 3a, 4a, 4b, 4e, 9a, 9b, 10b, 12e)	/oo/ (2c, 3e, 7e, 8b, 8e, 13d)
_____	_____	_____
_____	_____	_____
_____	_____	_____

/oo/ (9c, 10e)	/aw/ (1b, 2b, 8a, 8d)	/ou/ (2e, 10a)
/oi/ (10b, 10c)	/ar/ (4a, 12c, 13b)	/er/ (1e, 4c, 5a, 6a, 6c, 6d, 7a, 7b, 8e, 9e, 10c, 11c)
/or/ (3d, 3d, 4d, 7d, 9d, 10d)	/air/ (4e, 5b)	/ə/ + /l/ (2e, 3b, 4b, 5e, 11d, 13a, 13d, 13e)

Syllabication (words with 2 or more syllabes)		
Closed Syllable/short (1a, 1b, 1c, 2a, 2b, 2c, 3b, 3c, 4a, 4e, 5a, 5c, 5d, 6a, 6c, 6d, 6e, 7a, 7b, 7e, 8a, 8b, 8c, 9a, 9d, 9e, 10d, 10e, 11c, 11d, 11e, 12a, 12b, 12c, 13a, 13b, 13c, 13e)	Open Syllable/long (1a, 2a, 3c, 4e, 5b, 6b, 6c, 6e, 7d, 8c, 8e, 9b, 10c, 12a, 13c, 13e)	Magic E and Digraph Syllable (1b, 1d, 1e, 2c, 2d, 2e, 3a, 4a, 4b, 4c, 5c, 5e, 6a, 6b, 7b, 7e, 8a, 8b, 8e, 10b, 10c, 10e, 12a, 12e, 12d)
R-Controlled Syllable (1e, 3d, 4a, 4c, 4e, 5a, 5b, 6a, 6c, 6d, 7a, 7b, 7d, 8e, 9d, 9e, 10c, 10d, 11c, 12c, 13b)	ə Syllable (1c, 2d, 2e, 3a, 4b, 5e, 9a, 9b, 10b, 12e, 13d)	—le Syllable (3b, 11d, 13a, 13e)

End-of-Year Fluency Assessment
The Elephant and the Ape

"Look at me!" cried Tusk the elephant. "See how big and strong I am!"	14
"Look at me!" cried his friend Nim the ape. "See how quick and clever I am!"	30
"It is better to be big and strong than quick and clever!" said Tusk.	44
"Not so," answered Nim. "It is better to be quick and clever than big and strong."	60
So the two friends began to argue.	67
"Let's not argue," said Nim. "Let's go to Sage and ask him to settle the matter."	83
"Agreed!" said Tusk and off they ran.	90
Sage was a wise old owl who lived in the darkest corner of an old tower.	106
Sage listened to what Tusk and Nim had to say.	116

"I see," he said. "There is way to settle this. You must do just as I say. Then, I shall 136
ell you which is better." 141

"Agreed!" said Tusk. 144

"Agreed!" said Nim. 147

"Cross the river," said Sage, "and pick me some of the mangoes that grow on the 163
reat tree." 165

Tusk and Nim set off on their mission. 173

Soon, they came to the river, which was very wide and deep. Nim was afraid. 188

"I can't cross that river!" he cried. "Let's go back." 198

Tusk laughed. "Didn't I tell you it is better to be big and strong than to be quick and 217
lever? It is an easy thing for me to cross the river." 229

Tusk lifted Nim up with his trunk and put him on his broad back. Then, he swam 246
cross the river. 249

Soon, they came to the mango tree. It was so tall that Tusk could not reach the mangoes, even with his long trunk. He tried to knock the tree over but could not do it. 265 281 284

"I can't reach the mangoes," he said. "The tree is too high. We shall have to go back without the mangoes." 300 305

Nim laughed. "Didn't I tell you it is better to be quick and clever than big and strong? It is an easy thing for me to climb this tree." 321 334

Nim scampered up the tree and tossed down a whole basketful of ripe mangoes. Tusk picked them up. Then, the two of them the crossed the river as before. 347 362 363

When they came again to Sage's tower, Tusk said, "Here are your mangoes. Now tell us which is better—to be big and strong or to be quick and clever?" 376 393

Sage answered, "I should think you would know that yourself. You crossed the river, and Nim gathered the fruit. Sometimes it is better to be big and strong and sometimes it is better to be quick and clever. Each thing in its place is best." 405 421 438

"That is true," answered Tusk. 443

"Indeed it is," said Nim. 448

Then, away they went, and from that day on, they were better friends than ever before. 462 464

End-of-Year Morphology Assessment

1. Which of the following words has the prefix *un–*, meaning "not," as in the word *unsafe*?

    A.   understand

    B.   unable

    C.   uncle

    D.   under

2. If someone is giving *nonverbal* signals, how are they giving signals?

_____

3. If you want to *rewrite* something, what do you want to do?

    A.   write it above

    B.   write it below

    C.   write it again

    D.   write it big

4. Which of the following words correctly fits in the sentence below?

> The recipe said to _____ the oven to 350° while prepping the food for baking.

    A.   preheat

    B.   preschool

    C.   preview

    D.   preselect

5. Choose the phrase that is an example of what the word **disobey** means.

    A.   unplugging the printer from the computer

    B.   saying no thank you to a vegetable you don't like

    C.   sharing your toys with a younger sibling

    D.   not cleaning your room after your mom says you have to

6. When you add the prefix *mis–* to the verb *behave*, the new word is **misbehave**. What part of speech is **misbehave**?

_____

7. Which of the following words have suffixes that both mean "a person who?"

    A.   *dirty* and *coastal*

    B.   *farmer* and *actor*

    C.   *dangerous* and *decorative*

    D.   *stylish* and *loneliness*

8. What is the root word and part of speech of the underlined word in the following sentence?

> Sometimes, the <u>counselor</u> at school comes to our class to teach lessons about being a good person and helping others.

Root Word: _____

Part of Speech of **counselor**: _____

9. An *artist* is a person who _____.

    A.   erases art

    B.   makes or creates art

    C.   is full of art

    D.   lacks art

10. If you are skilled in pediatrics, or the branch of medicine dealing with babies and children, what are you?

    A.   a cosmetician

    B.   a politician

    C.   a pediatrician

    D.   a musician

11. Circle the word that has the suffix –*y*, which means "full of or covered with," correctly added to the root word?

    rusty   sorry   happy   story

12. Which of the following choices is a *nutritional* food choice?

    A.   potato chips

    B.   ice cream

    C.   a lollipop

    D.   asparagus

13. What word means "full of danger?"

_____

14. Add the correct suffix or suffixes to the root word by writing on the blank to complete the sentence.

| She humor_____ presented the results of her study and kept the audience interested and entertained. |

    –ous   –ive   –ly   –y   –al

15. If you are **creatively** decorating a room, how are you decorating a room?

_____

16. The _____ cut on my hand hurt even more when Mom started to clean it.

    A.   painful

    B.   careless

    C.   hopeful

    D.   fearless

17. Which of the following words correctly fits in the sentence below?

> I gave my mother a _____ look when she told me I had to finish my science project before I could go to the soccer game; I knew I still had a lot of work and would not be able to go to the game.

- A.   fearless
- B.   careless
- C.   painless
- D.   hopeless

18. Complete this sentence:

My brother acted in a ***selfish*** way when he _____

_____.

19. Which of the following might cause ***loneliness*** to set in?

- A.   All of your friends left.
- B.   You took the dog for a walk.
- C.   Your neighbor invited you to join a book club.
- D.   The baseball game went into extra innings.

20. If something is ***chewable***, that means it is _____

_____.

21. When adding the suffix *–ible* to the verb *flex*, you create ***flexible***. What part of speech is the root word and the new word?

flex Part of Speech: _____

flexible Part of Speech: _____

22. Which of the following words with the prefix *pro–* means "to move forward?"

    A. proceed

    B. project

    C. proposal

    D. provide

23. If you need an ***antidote***, what might have happened?

    A.   You might have eaten a salad for lunch.

    B.   You might have cut your finger on a thorn from a rosebush.

    C.   You might have fallen asleep on the couch.

    D.   You might have been bitten by a poisonous snake.

24. How many wheels does a ***unicycle*** have?   _____

25. My father is ***bilingual*** so that means he can speak _____ languages.

26. Rachel's favorite author just published a ***trilogy***, which is a series of _____ books.

27. What type of literature includes selections that reflect many cultures?

    A.   multicultural

    B.   agricultural

    C.   subcultural

    D.   cultural

28. Which of the following words correctly fits in the sentence below?

> Mom insisted that Dad stop mowing the lawn to drink some water because she was worried he would _____ on such a hot day.

    A.   overeat

    B.   underestimate

    C.   overheat

    D.   underline

29. When adding the prefix *mid–* to the noun *field*, you create **midfield**. What part of speech is the word **midfield**?

    A.   noun

    B.   adjective

    C.   verb

    D.   adverb

30. What type of camera would you need to buy if you wanted to take pictures of fish and plants in the ocean on your vacation?

    A.   an overpowered camera

    B.   an underwater camera

    C.   an underpowered camera

    D.   an overfish camera

The Balance of Nature

1. What would happen to the Mara National Reserve ecosystem if all of the

cheetahs were hunted to extinction? _____

_____

_____

2. Why are ants important to the acacia tree? _____

_____

_____

      Page _____

3. Why are people not allowed to build towns or major roads inside a

preserve? _____

_____

4. What might happen if people were allowed to build towns or major

roads inside a preserve? _____

_____

_____

5. What would happen if all of the big cats disappeared from the savanna?

_____

_____

_____

Page _____

Subject and Object Pronouns

Rewrite the sentence replacing the underlined word or words with a subject or object pronoun.

1. <u>My older brother</u> helps me with my math homework.

_____

_____

2. I wish I could help <u>my older brother</u> with something too!

_____

_____

3. <u>Mrs. Smalley</u> is the best neighbor ever!

_____

_____

4. The whole neighborhood would like to have a party for <u>Mrs. Smalley</u>.

_____

_____

5. <u>That tree house</u> was awesome!

_____

_____

6. I wish we could build <u>that tree house</u> in our yard!

_____

_____

Word Sort

Read the words in the box and circle the letters that have the sound /aw/. Write the words under each header that match the header's spelling pattern.

'au' > /aw/	'aw' > /aw/	'al' > /aw/	'ough' > /aw/	'augh' > /aw/
_____	_____	_____	_____	_____
_____	_____	_____	_____	_____
_____	_____	_____	_____	_____
_____	_____	_____	_____	_____
_____	_____	_____	_____	_____
_____	_____	_____	_____	_____
_____	_____	_____	_____	_____

outlaw	enough	maul	mall	capable	honest
auditory	yawning	laughter	awhile	fought	frown
almost	forethought	sausage	claws	walk	stepdaughter
alligator	auction	brought	stalling	tough	sprawl
haughty	chalk	shallow	applause	cough	thoughtless
dough	California	audition	brawl	awesome	doubt

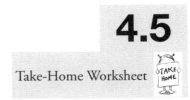

The Balance of Nature

This photo was taken in Kenya, a country in east Africa. Kenya is famous for the **wildlife** on its grasslands. When people visit Kenya, they often go on **safari** to see the animals.

A large portion of Kenya is part of the Mara National **Reserve**. A **reserve** is a protected area of land. People are not allowed to build towns or major roads there. The land is set aside for nature, especially the animals.

Most of the Mara is open grassland, known as a savanna. The land is basically flat, with gently rolling hills. There are some trees and bushes growing in the savanna, but it is mostly grass.

In many ways, the savanna ecosystem is like any other ecosystem. There are food chains with producers, consumers, and decomposers.

Huge **herds** of **wildebeests**, zebras, and other consumers eat the savanna grass. There is plenty of grass for everyone. This also means there is plenty of meat for the lions!

The Mara is known for its many types of **acacia** trees. Giraffes like to eat **acacia** leaves.

Some ants in the Mara like to eat certain **acacia** seeds. The ants carry the seeds underground. They eat the fruit that surrounds the seed, but they do not hurt the seed itself. Instead, they leave it there in the ground where they ate it. That's how some **acacias** spread their seeds! This is another example of a way in which organisms **rely on** each other in an ecosystem.

Each living thing in a healthy ecosystem can survive with help from other living things. The living things depend on each other. Of course, not all living things survive for very long. Many critters are eaten by bigger animals. Most seeds do not sprout. But enough will survive to make sure life continues in the ecosystem.

The savanna's grass eaters would probably be happy if all the big cats disappeared. However, if all the big cats disappeared from the Mara, this would **upset** the natural **balance** in the food chain.

Cheetahs and other predators hunt the weak, sick, and young members of the **herd**. As a result, the strong animals in the **herd** tend to survive and have healthy young.

No **gazelle** wants to be eaten by a lion or cheetah. But in an ecosystem, the predators help keep the population from getting out of control. If there were too many **gazelles**, then all **gazelles** might have trouble finding enough food. Cheetahs help make sure there aren't too many **gazelles**!

The grasslands of the Mara National **Reserve** seem to stretch on forever. It is hard to imagine anything bad ever happening to **upset** the ecosystem of this vast, beautiful land. But if nothing bad ever happened, then the government of Kenya would not have bothered making this a **reserve**. Many animals were illegally hunted to near **extinction**. The people of Kenya had to set the land apart in order to protect the ecosystem and all the animals in it.

Spelling Assessment

As your teacher calls out the words, write them under the correct header.

'ough' > /aw/	'au' > /aw/	'augh' > /aw/	'aw' > /aw/	'al' > /aw/
_____	_____	_____	_____	_____
_____	_____	_____	_____	_____
_____	_____	_____	_____	_____
_____	_____	_____	_____	_____
_____	_____	_____	_____	_____
_____	_____	_____	_____	_____

Challenge Word: _____   **Challenge Word:** _____

Content Word: _____

Dictated Sentences:

1. _____

   _____.

2. _____

   _____.

Natural Changes to the Environment

Read the following statements, write *true* or *false*, and write the page number that has the answer.

	True or False	Page Number
Water is one of nature's weakest forces.		
Erosion is one common force of nature.		
Petrified means turned to stone.		
When the land changes, the ecology changes.		
Living things usually cannot find a way to adapt.		

1. Organize the following into a food chain from the Petrified Forest: snake, bird, coyote, seeds

    A.   Apex predator: _____

    B.   _____

    C.   _____

    D.   _____

2. What happens during a big flood? _____

_____

_____

3. Write the main idea of this chapter. _____

_____

_____

Subject and Object Pronouns

Write the pronoun on the blank that correctly completes the sentence. Then, circle *subject pronoun* or *object pronoun*.

1. _____ has studied ballet for many years.
    (She, Her)

    Subject Pronoun   Object Pronoun

2. The story of the magical birds is interesting to _____.
    (him, he)

    Subject Pronoun   Object Pronoun

3. Our pet snake escaped from the cage and no one could find _____
    (them, it.)

    Subject Pronoun   Object Pronoun

4. _____ were the only ones brave enough to dive from the diving board.
    (They, Me)

    Subject Pronoun   Object Pronoun

5. _____ enjoy playing football in the backyard with friends.
    (We, Us)

    Subject Pronoun   Object Pronoun

6. When children hide, it is very difficult to find _____.
    (we, them)

    Subject Pronoun   Object Pronoun

7. _____ should be very happy to hear such great news!
    (You, Me)

    Subject Pronoun   Object Pronoun

8.   Because it is summer, _____ garden, swim, and enjoy the sunshine.
                              (him, I)

Subject Pronoun   *Object Pronoun*

Dictionary Skills

Use the following example to complete the sentences that follow.

Example:

   foul—*adjective*: 1. disgusting 2. dirty 3. stormy 4. against the rules (sports or games) *verb*: 5. to make something dirty 6. to go against the rules (sports or games) 7. to hit a ball out of bounds (baseball) *noun*: 8. a breaking of the rules or boundaries (sports or games) (*adjective*: **fouler**, **foulest** verb: **fouled** *noun*: **fouls**)

1. Dakota hit three _____ in the first inning. (____) _____

2. The weather was _____ outside. (____) _____

3. After working in the muddy fields, he had the _____ boots I've ever
   seen! (____) _____

---

awkward—*adjective*: 1. embarrassing 2. difficult to handle 3. clumsy; not graceful
   4. unable to talk with people easily (*adverb*: **awkwardly**, *noun*: **awkwardness**)

caution—*noun*: 1. carefulness to avoid danger; *verb*: 2. to warn against danger:
   cautioned, **cautioning**

cautious—*adjective*: careful (*adverb*: **cautiously**)

naughty—*adjective*: 1. disobedient 2. not proper: **naughtier**, **naughtiest** (*adverb*:
   naughtily, *noun*: **naughtiness**)

1.   Monty walked very slowly and _____ through the long, dark, and winding hallway. (__) _____

2.   Jessica told the teacher in the cafeteria that her friend said a _____ word at lunch today. (__) _____

3.   Using a paint brush can be _____ until you have plenty of practice.(__) _____

4.   It was an _____ moment when Willie spilled his milk all over Mrs. Thompson. (__) _____

5.   Kirbie was the _____ puppy at obedience school. (__) _____

Write sentences using two forms of the words that were not used in the sentences above.

1. _____

_____

_____

2. _____

_____

_____

Anticipation Guide for "Human Changes to the Environment"

Before Reading		Statement	After Reading		
True	False		True	False	Page
		A tool is a kind of technology.			
		Humans control all of nature to meet their needs.			
		The biggest dam in America is the Colorado Dam.			
		A dam is good for people but not so good for the environment.			
		The Colorado Dam is built across the Hoover River.			

1. Give one example of how humans use technology to change or control nature.

    _____

    _____

    _____

2. List two ways that the biggest dam in America is good for people.

    _____

    _____

    _____

3. List three ways that the biggest dam in America is not good for the environment.

    _____

    _____

    _____

Dear Family Member,

Please help your child succeed in spelling by taking a few minutes each evening to review the words together. Helpful activities for your child to do include: spelling the words orally, writing sentences using the words, or simply copying the words.

Spelling Words

This week, we are reviewing the spelling patterns of /oi/, /ou/, and /aw/ that we have already learned. On Friday, your child will be assessed on these words.

Students have been assigned three Challenge Words, *usually*, *bye*, and *buy*. Challenge Words are words used very often. The Challenge Words do not follow the spelling patterns for this week and need to be memorized.

The Content Word for this week is *environment*. *Environment* does not follow the spelling pattern for this week. This word is directly related to the material that we are reading in *Introduction to Ecology*. The Content Word is an optional spelling word for your child. If your child would like to try it but gets it incorrect, it will not count against him or her on the assessment. We encourage everyone to stretch themselves a bit and try to spell this word.

The spelling words, including the Challenge Words and the Content Word, are listed below:

1. loyalty
2. boundaries
3. foundation
4. brought
5. squawked
6. disappoint
7. author
8. turquoise
9. allowance
10. employee
11. default
12. towering
13. embroidery
14. announcement
15. cowardly
16. accountable
17. corduroy
18. **Challenge Word**: usually
19. **Challenge Word**: bye
20. **Challenge Word**: buy

Content Word: environment

Student Reader

This week, we are continuing our unit on ecology. Your child will be learning about how humans have made changes to the environment and how we can protect our environment and ecosystems. Your child will also read a biography of John Muir. Be sure to ask your child each evening about what he or she is learning.

Students will take home text copies of the chapters in the Reader throughout the unit. Encouraging students to read a text directly related to this domain-based unit will provide content and vocabulary reinforcement. Please remind your child that the glossary can be used for finding the meaning of the bolded words.

Natural Changes to the Environment

Ecosystems can be **fragile**. It doesn't take much to cause big changes in the environment. Sometimes the ecosystem can recover from a change. Sometimes the change is forever.

Erosion is one **common force** of nature. Over time, the land on either side of a stream can **erode**. When it rains really hard a little stream can fill with water and flood. A **flood** may last for an hour. It may last for a few days.

The plants on a hillside have roots that reach deep into the soil. The roots hold the soil together. When it rains, or when the wind blows really hard, the plant roots hold the soil in place. Without plants, the soil starts to **erode**.

Water is one of nature's most powerful **forces**. During a big **flood**, the entire **landscape** can be changed. A flooded river can tear apart plants, trees, and soil.

First, the **topsoil** is removed. This is the richest soil, where you find most of the nutrients and **decaying** matter. Once the **topsoil** is washed away, the **forces** of nature slowly eat away at the clay and rock underneath.

This is from **Petrified** Forest National Park in Arizona. Throughout the park, there are ancient trees that have turned to stone. The trees have been **petrified**!

These may look like normal rocks but they're not! There was a forest ecosystem here about 200 million years ago, when some of the first dinosaurs roamed the earth. These rocks are actually pieces of **prehistoric** trees!

Back then, there were producers, consumers, and decomposers, too! Fossils found in the **Petrified** Forest show that there were swamp plants, like ferns. There were also dinosaurs that looked sort of like crocodiles.

At some point, the area was flooded by huge amounts of water and mud. The trees were covered. The entire forest was destroyed, along with the food chain. All that mud covering the trees dried. Over millions of years, the mud turned to rock. Instead of rotting, the trees turned to rock, too!

Millions of years and **countless floods** later, the land in **Petrified** Forest National Park has **eroded**. We are left with this strange **landscape**. It is still called a forest, but many of the trees are really rocks.

The land is almost like a desert. However, the **Petrified** Forest does get some rain. There is actually a lot happening in this ecosystem, even though it looks like a dry, sandy place. There are 500 different **species** of plants in **Petrified** Forest National Park. There are no dinosaurs, but there are little lizards. There are also toads, snakes, birds, and **jackrabbits**. Coyotes are near the top of the food chain. They eat just about anything, meat and plant alike.

The **Petrified** Forest is interesting because it shows how nature's **forces** can change the **landscape**. When the land changes, the ecology changes. There were once forests and swamps here. Now, it is a rocky desert. The hills have **eroded**. Much of the rich soil has been washed away, leaving mostly sand and rocks. But it is still an ecosystem! Through all the changes, there has always been life here. Living things find a way to adapt and survive.

Human Changes to the Environment

As you have learned, every plant and animal in a natural ecosystem depends on other plants or animals for its survival. For example, a butterfly depends on a flower's nectar for food. At the same time, a flower depends on butterflies and other insects to spread its pollen.

Thousands of years ago, early humans were like all other living things in nature. They were just another part of the natural food chain. They hunted animals and gathered plants for food. They made shelters and clothing using the materials in their environment. Most importantly, they used only what they needed for basic survival.

However, humans also had the ability to create and use **technology**. At first, they used simple **technology**, like tools made of stone and wood. These tools made it easier to hunt, build, and do other things for survival.

Over time, **technology** improved. Humans learned to create and use machines. Instead of hunting animals, they learned to raise animals like cows and chickens for food. Instead of gathering nuts, berries, and roots, they learned to grow their own crops. In other words, humans learned to change and control some parts of nature in order to meet their needs.

With **technology**, humans were able to change the environment. The land in this picture may have been a forest or natural grassland. Now, instead, it is a wheat field. Insects and other organisms still live in the soil and feed on the wheat plants. However, this is not what you might call a natural field. Humans planted the seeds in this field and humans decide when to harvest the crops to make food.

The land beneath any town or city was once a natural ecosystem. Then, humans came along and used **technology** to change the natural environment. There are some trees, grass, and flowers in a city. But they are only there because people want them there. Some animals, like squirrels and birds, also live in cities alongside humans. But these creatures had to learn to survive in an environment created by humans.

Now, with all our cities and **technology**, it is sometimes easy for us to forget about nature and ecosystems. It is easy for us to think of nature as something we can visit, but not something we are really part of.

It is also easy for us to think of nature as a **resource primarily** for humans—something we can use and change to suit our needs. This image shows one of the most amazing things ever built in America: the Hoover Dam. There are thousands of dams in America but the Hoover Dam is the biggest. It was built across the mighty Colorado River. It **generates hydroelectric** power, or electricity, for over a million people in Arizona, Nevada, and California. The **reservoir** created by the dam also provides water for thousands of homes and farms.

The Hoover Dam is very important for people who depend on it for water and electricity. But the dam also changed the landscape and ecology along the Colorado River forever. It changed the natural flow of the river and **endangered** several species of fish and plants. You can say the dam was good for people but not so good for the environment. Either way, it is here to stay and it is a good example of a way in which people can change the natural environment.

The people in this little town live in a very beautiful place surrounded by a natural ecosystem. They have their houses and roads and they have cleared away some of the forest to make **pastures** for animals or farming. But most of the surrounding land still belongs to nature.

Not all environmental changes caused by humans are bad for the environment. It is certainly possible for people to survive and enjoy life while helping to protect the balance of nature. In the next three chapters, you will learn more about the damage people can do to ecosystems and, more importantly, the things we can do to protect them.

Environmental Damage Caused by Humans

Describe what happened to each of the following when the *Deepwater Horizon* exploded:

People _____

_____

Oil from deep in the ground _____

_____

Water near the rig _____

_____

Fish in the water near the rig _____

_____

Gulf Coast _____

_____

Birds living near the Gulf Coast _____

_____

Wetlands along the Gulf Coast _____

_____

Comparative and Superlative Adjectives and Adverbs

Choose from the options in parentheses to complete the sentence.

1. The red paint is _____ than the yellow paint.
   (brighter, more brightly)

2. The painted poster shines _____ than the unpainted poster.
   (brighter, more brightly)

3. The cold wind is _____ on my dry skin than on your skin.
   (harsher, more harshly)

4. The wind blows _____ in cold weather than in warm weather.
   (harsher, more harshly)

5. In the race, the hare is _____ than the tortoise.
   (quicker, more quickly)

6. In the race, the hare runs _____ than the tortoise.
   (quicker, more quickly)

7. Sam is a _____ person than his brother.
   (kinder, more kindly)

8. Sam always treats me _____ than his brother.
   (kinder, more kindly)

Name: _____

 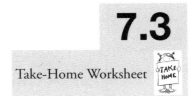

Environmental Damage Caused by Humans

Most of the vehicles you see every day—from boats and trains to cars and planes—have one thing in common: they need gasoline in order to operate. A car's engine burns gasoline. The energy from burning gasoline makes the car move. Gasoline is made from oil, which is thick, black liquid that can be found deep underground in certain places on Earth.

Getting oil out of the ground is not easy. People get oil by drilling wells deep into the earth. The wells suck oil up from underground. Thousands of oil wells are used to **pump** oil out of the ground all over the world.

A lot of oil is located in the earth's crust deep beneath the ocean waters. This is a picture of an **oil rig**, or oil platform. It is **anchored** far out in the ocean. Dozens of workers live on the **oil rig** for months at a time. They use a special type of drill to get oil from hundreds or even thousands of feet beneath the ocean surface.

Unfortunately, drilling for oil is not only difficult but also dangerous. This danger became reality on April 20, 2010, when a terrible accident happened on an **oil rig** called the *Deepwater Horizon.*

The *Deepwater Horizon* was owned by a company called BP. It was **anchored** in the Gulf of Mexico, about 40 miles off the coast of Louisiana. An important piece of equipment deep underwater broke, allowing oil and natural gases to escape from the earth. This caused a huge explosion on the **oil rig**. The *Deepwater Horizon* was destroyed by the explosion and fire that followed. Tragically, 11 men died in the explosion and 16 others were badly injured. But this was not the end of the story. The **disaster** that followed was a massive **oil spill**.

When the rig exploded, oil began flowing freely from inside the earth. Because it was so far underwater, nobody knew how to stop the oil from flowing. Within days, the waters near the damaged well were heavily **polluted** with thick, black oil. Oil continued to spill into the water for three months and the oil quickly spread.

The ocean ecosystem is fragile. Everything from microorganisms to plants and fish rely on clean water in order to survive. The oil threatened fish and all other life in the nearby waters. Within days, oil from the **oil spill** washed up all along the Gulf Coast of the United States. The oil washed up on beaches in Texas, Louisiana, Mississippi, Alabama, and Florida. At the same time, the oil threatened the lives of fish, birds, and other wildlife in or near the water.

The grassy, shallow wetlands along the Gulf Coast are home to a fragile ecosystem with a huge **variety** of wildlife. People were especially worried about the **effects** oil might have on this area.

In the wetlands, you can find all sorts of shellfish, including oysters, crabs, and shrimp. You can find many birds, including herons, pelicans, and egrets, like the ones in this image. Reptiles such as alligators and snakes, as well as many mammals, also rely on the Gulf Coast wetlands for food and shelter. All of these animals can be harmed if they get covered in oil or if they eat other animals that are covered in oil.

Furthermore, the wetlands are very important for people. They are an important **source** of seafood, such as the shrimp you might order in a restaurant.

The wetlands are important for other reasons as well. The grass roots keep the sand and soil in place. If the grasses get covered in oil, they could die. Then, the sand and soil would wash away. As a result, the **coastline** could erode, harming nearby towns and cities.

So, oil from the **oil spill** posed a threat to life at sea and on land, including people. This was a huge problem and everyone knew something had to be done to protect the wetlands and wildlife from the oil. In the next chapter, you will learn what people did to save the Gulf Coast from the **oil spill**. You will also learn about other things people can do to protect all kinds of ecosystems from human activities.

Protecting the Environment

1. Write the main idea of this chapter. _____

_____

_____

2. What will probably happen to the wetlands that were damaged? _____

_____

_____

3. What is an appropriate title for the list below?

Title: _____

Section 1—Trees have been recently cut down.

Section 2—Trees have been left standing.

Section 3—New trees have been planted.

    A.   Sections of an Oil Rig

    B.   Sections of a Tree Farm

    C.   Sections of a National Park

    D.   Sections of a Wildlife Reserve

4. What other things from nature besides oil and coal can we use to generate

electricity? _____

_____

_____

5. What is an oil boom? _____

_____

_____

Page _____

Prefix Review: *uni–*, *bi–*, *tri–*, *multi–*, *over–*, *mid–*, and *under–*

Directions:

1. Throw the die and move the number of spaces indicated.
2. Read the word in the space that you land on and use it correctly in a sentence.
3. Then, write the word in the correct column on this page or the next.
4. Next, write the part of speech for the way you used the word in the sentence.

uni–	Part of Speech	*bi–*	Part of Speech	*tri–*	Part of Speech

Name: _____

multi–	Part of Speech	over–	Part of Speech	mid–	Part of Speech	under–	Part of Speech

multivitamin

removable

overcharge

Good job! You got a big tree for the beavers. Move ahead one space.

underwa

underline

uniform

bimonthly

midtown

unicycle

YOU WIN!

Frisky Beavers

Oh no! The tree fell on the den. Wait 1 turn.

underpowered

trilogy

overeat

multiling

Name: _____

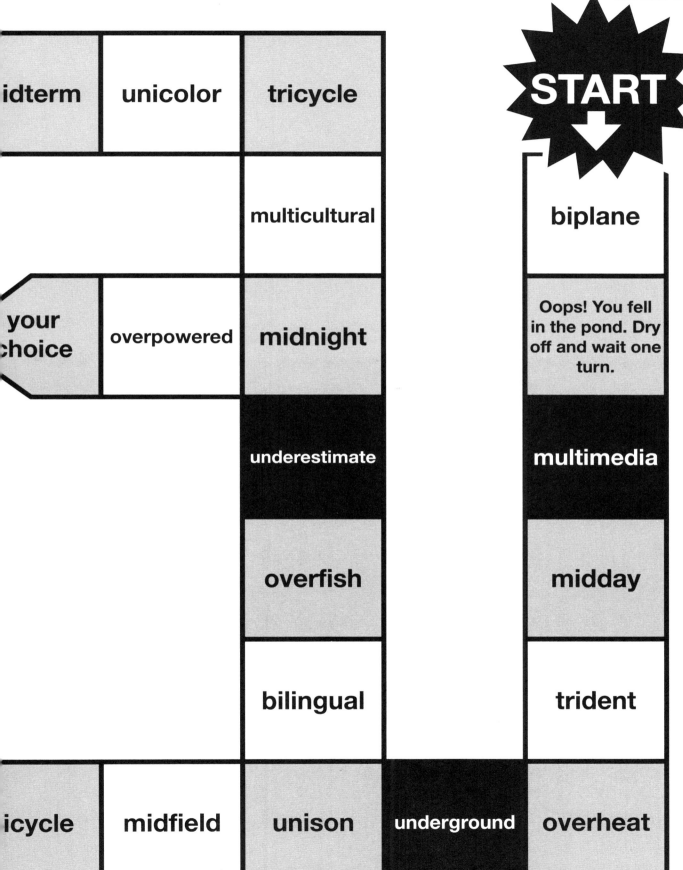

idterm | unicolor | tricycle

multicultural

START

biplane

your choice | overpowered | **midnight**

Oops! You fell in the pond. Dry off and wait one turn.

underestimate

multimedia

overfish

midday

bilingual

trident

icycle | **midfield** | **unison** | underground | **overheat**

Blank Busters

loyalty	boundaries	foundation	brought
squawked	disappoint	author	turquoise
allowance	employee	default	towering
embroidery	announcement	cowardly	accountable
corduroy			

Challenge Word: usually
Challenge Word: bye
Challenge Word: buy
Content Word: environment

Fill in the blanks in the sentences below with one of the spelling words in the chart. Only if needed, add a suffix to the end of a word, or change the word form, in order for the sentence to make sense: *–s, –ed, –ing, –er, –ly,* and *–ous.*

1. My grandmother is very skilled at _____ and has made many things like pillows, items to hang on the wall, and other things just with a needle and thread!

2. Keisha saved her _____ and bought her mom a _____ bracelet for her birthday.

3. When fall arrived, Mom bought me a new pair of brown _____ pants that are warm and comfortable for the change in temperature.

4. My favorite _____ has a new book out about poison dart frogs in the rainforest.

5. _____, I eat my breakfast first and then brush my teeth.

6.   The bird in the tree _____ as the cat crept along the ground, trying to hide itself.

7.   The manager of the food store was _____ when his _____ was sick and couldn't attend the annual picnic.

8.   The printer always starts at the _____setting, which is the standard setting for printing in black and white ink.

9.   The boys' _____ were with their families first and their friends second.

10. In the story, the mouse acted in a _____ way when he first promised to help fight the cat but then ran away as soon as a threat of danger presented itself.

Write three sentences using spelling words of your choice that were not used in the first ten sentences. Make sure to use correct capitalization and punctuation. You may use the Challenge Words or Content Word in your sentences.

1.   _____

2.   _____

3.   _____

_____

Protecting the Environment

After three months, engineers, scientists, and other experts from all over the United States and around the world finally managed to stop the oil spill from the *Deepwater Horizon* oil rig. They **sealed** off the well so the oil does not leak into the water anymore.

Through those difficult months, people worked hard to protect the waters and beaches around the Gulf of Mexico. One of the first things they did was to spread **oil booms** in the water. An **oil boom** is like a floating wall or barrier used to contain the spread of oil. **Oil booms** were spread all along the coast in an effort to keep oil away from the beaches and wetlands. Once the oil was trapped within the **oil booms**, special boats came along and cleaned the oil out of the water.

Still, thousands of gallons of oil from the oil spill washed up on land. Workers spent months cleaning oil from the beaches. Luckily, thanks to lots of hard work and determination, people were able to prevent a total environmental disaster. We will never know exactly how many fish, shrimp, and other animals were killed by the oil spill, but we do know that it could have been worse. Most importantly, most of the wetlands were saved and those that were damaged will probably **recover**.

There are many things you can do to help protect the environment. To make the things we use every day—like bottles, cans, and paper—we need to use **natural resources**. To make cans, people need to dig mines in the earth and remove metals like aluminum and iron. To make paper and cardboard, people cut down trees. Think about all the plastic you use: bottles, bags, toys, furniture, and so many other things. Plastic is made from oil, the same kind of oil that goes into your car's engine.

Cans, bottles, papers, and boxes can be **recycled** and turned into new cans, bottles, papers, and boxes. This means less metal needs to be mined, fewer trees need to be cut down, and less oil needs to be used to make plastics. This helps protect the environment!

Recycling is important, but unfortunately, it is not enough to protect the earth's ecosystems. Today, there are over 7 billion people on the planet. About half of all the land on Earth is used to grow food for all those people. Towns, cities, and roads cover a lot of the remaining land. That does not leave much room for forests, grasslands, and other natural ecosystems.

This is a tree farm. It is one example of the many ways in which people can protect nature while using its valuable resources. The tree farm has three sections. In one section, you can see where the loggers recently cut down all the trees. In another section, they left the trees standing. They will come back and cut those trees down in a few years. In the third section, they planted new trees. Some day, those trees will be big enough to cut down. By then, the loggers will have planted more trees. Using tree farms like this, people can keep using the same land to get the wood they need without having to find new forests to cut down.

People are also working hard to find cleaner, safer ways to fuel our vehicles and provide electricity for our homes, schools, and businesses. Today, most fuel comes from oil and coal. As you learned, getting these fuels can lead to terrible accidents.

Fortunately, oil and coal aren't our only choices. We can also use the wind and sun to generate electricity. This picture shows a wind farm. The giant windmills are used to generate clean, safe electricity for people's homes. We will continue to use oil and coal for many years to come, but little by little we are finding safer, cleaner **alternatives**.

It is possible to protect the environment and get all the food and fuel we need in order to live happy, healthy lives. To do this, we need to understand what we can do to help maintain the balance of nature and avoid causing **unnecessary** damage.

John Muir

1. List three reasons bald eagles became endangered.

    A.   _____

    B.   _____

    C.   _____

Page _____

2. Why might the landscape of the Sierra Nevada Mountains have inspired John

Muir to start the Sierra Club? _____

_____

3. Conservationists are people who _____

_____.

Page _____

4. Write the main idea of this chapter. _____

_____

5. How are you willing to work to help protect America's natural ecological treasures?

_____

_____

Write a Letter

_____

_____

_____

(Heading)

_____

(Greeting)

_____

_____

_____

_____

(Body)

_____

(Closing)

_____

(Signature)

Prefix Review

Circle the correct word, from the choices after each sentence, to complete the sentence.

1.	The performer rode his _____ in circles while juggling three balls.	cycle	unicycle
2.	She is _____ and can speak two languages, English and Spanish.	bilingual	multilingual
3.	During the winter, there is less light during the _____ than in the summer.	midday	day
4.	The second movie in the _____ will be released this year, with the third coming out the following year.	trident	trilogy
5.	The _____ power lines were protected when the hurricane made landfall and caused massive damage.	underground	ground
6.	Every year, the school hosts a _____ fair to celebrate the diverse backgrounds of students.	cultural	multicultural
7.	Grandma said to only pick a few things to eat at a time during the picnic so we would not _____ and be able to play games later.	overeat	eat
8.	A _____ has three sides while a square has four sides.	tricycle	triangle

Write the part of speech and the meaning for each word. Then, write the root word for each word.

1. *midfield*

Part of Speech: _____   Root Word: _____

Meaning: _____

2. *biplane*

Part of Speech: _____   Root Word: _____

Meaning: _____

3. *underline*

Part of Speech: _____   Root Word: _____

Meaning: _____

4. *overcharge*

Part of Speech: _____   Root Word: _____

Meaning: _____

Word Sort

Read the words in the box and circle the letters that have the sounds /aw/, /oi/, or /ou/. Write the words under each header that match the header's spelling pattern.

/oi/	**/ou/**	**/aw/**
_____	_____	_____
_____	_____	_____
_____	_____	_____
_____	_____	_____
_____	_____	_____
_____	_____	_____
_____	_____	_____
_____	_____	_____
_____	_____	_____
_____	_____	_____

sawmill	swagger	broiler	avoided	ought	meowed
buoy	rawhide	crouch	default	animal	housekeeper
rough	oiliest	destroyer	wrought	unsoiled	doubtful
crowded	automatic	laughter	biography	recalled	unemployed
sounding	rough	almost	crawled	voyage	yodel
rejoined	salamander	applause	frowned	fought	football

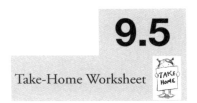

John Muir

This is a picture of the grand Yosemite Valley. It is in Yosemite National Park, a huge national park in California. It is easy to see why people fall in love with Yosemite and consider it to be America's most beautiful national park. Yosemite is also home to a rich ecosystem.

Some day you might get a chance to visit Yosemite. If you are very lucky, you may see a mountain lion. This is America's big cat. It's not as big as an African lion but it is still at the top of the Yosemite food chain.

You are far more likely to see squirrels in Yosemite. There are oak trees and acorns in Yosemite, but there are also plenty of other seeds and grains to eat and bury.

John Muir was not the first American to discover the beauty of Yosemite. However, he was one of the first to declare that it was a natural **treasure**. More importantly, he worked to make sure Yosemite and other special lands were protected forever.

John Muir was born in Scotland. In 1849, when he was 10 years old, his family moved to the United States. They lived on a farm in Wisconsin. John Muir loved reading as much as he loved nature. He grew up reading books by famous American **naturalists**. These books were all about plants, animals, and the forces of nature. Muir read books by two of America's most famous **naturalists**: Henry David Thoreau and Ralph Waldo Emerson.

When he was about 30 years old, Muir walked over one thousand miles from Indiana to Florida. He took what he called the "wildest, leafiest" way he could find and he loved every minute of it! A few years later, he wandered out to California.

In California, Muir hiked in the Sierra Nevada Mountains. This incredible landscape inspired him to start the Sierra Club. Today, the Sierra Club is America's oldest and largest environmental organization. It has thousands of members.

Muir became a well-known writer. He wrote books and articles about America's natural **treasures**. A few years after Muir started the Sierra Club, a man named Teddy Roosevelt was elected President of the United States. In the image on the next page, Roosevelt and Muir are posing for a picture in Yosemite.

Teddy Roosevelt and John Muir had a lot in common. They both loved nature. They were both **conservationists**, which means they wanted to protect natural **treasures**. Teddy Roosevelt used the power of the presidency to protect over 200 million acres of American **wilderness**.

American **conservationists** like Muir and Roosevelt have saved millions of acres from being paved over by cities and roads. They have also saved many important animals from extinction.

The bald eagle is the national bird of the United States. The eagle is a symbol of strength and freedom. There was a time not so long ago when the bald eagle was endangered, meaning that scientists were afraid it might become extinct, just like the dinosaurs.

Eagles became endangered for a number of reasons. People used to hunt eagles to make nice trophies for their living rooms. Pesticides and other chemical pollution harmed eagles as well. Lastly, eagles lost a lot of their habitat and nesting grounds due to farming and the growth of cities. About one hundred years ago, there were only a few eagles left.

Then, the U.S. Congress passed laws protecting bald eagles. It is illegal to hunt them. Farmers stopped using certain chemicals. Large areas of land, such as Yellowstone National Park and other parks, were reserved as habitats for eagles and other wildlife. All of this helped save the bald eagle population. Today, they are no longer in danger of becoming extinct, as long as people continue to be careful.

The eagle's history teaches an important story about protecting ecosystems. People almost caused eagles to become extinct. But through hard work and dedication, people also managed to save eagles. Today, we have eagles because some people cared enough to convince other Americans that the eagles were worth saving.

There are many incredible ecosystems to visit in the United States. They are all there thanks to the work of **conservationists** and groups like the Sierra Club. Are you willing to work to help protect America's natural ecological **treasures**?

Spelling Test

As your teacher calls out the words, write them in the correct column.

/oi/	/aw/	/ou/
_____	_____	_____
_____	_____	_____
_____	_____	_____
_____	_____	_____
_____	_____	_____
_____	_____	_____

Challenge Word: _____

Challenge Word: _____

Challenge Word: _____

Content Word: _____

Dictated Sentences

1. _____

_____

_____

_____

2. _____

_____

_____

_____

START ➡

correct

| Sorry, lose a turn |

correct

Ride the waterfall

incorrect

FINISH!

correct | incorrect

Tree falls! Lose a turn

incorrect | correct | **correct**

correct

incorrect | correct | Take a card from your opponent | correct | Sorry, lose a turn

Name: _____

ncorrect	correct	incorrect	Take another turn	correct

Match Me If You Can

incorrect
Give a card to your opponent
correct
incorrect
correct

correct	incorrect	correct	Take another turn	incorrect

10.3

Match Me if You Can Game Cards

Correct or Incorrect?
"The day is turning out to be my greatest day ever, said Fred, happily."

Correct or Incorrect?
Bananas, peaches, and grapes was my favorite fruits until now.

Correct or Incorrect?
This tomato has lots of light seeds.

Correct or Incorrect?
Connie, Carl and Chris are all members of the same family

Correct or Incorrect?
My grandma have lots of flowers in her garden.

Correct or Incorrect?
That movie was the mostest, bestest movie I've ever seen!

Correct or Incorrect?
"Are you ready for third grade?" asked my teacher?

Correct or Incorrect?
Summer are the best season of the year.

Correct or Incorrect?
The homework in my backpack was hard to find.

Correct or Incorrect?
Because I read that book five times, it was so funny.

Correct or Incorrect?
I like peanut butter, and jelly sandwiches, and lots of cold milk, for lunch.

Correct or Incorrect?
I has vegetables growing in my garden too.

Correct or Incorrect?
The silly frog asked, "Do you think it's fun being green?"

Correct or Incorrect?
I think its fun being such a great grammar student!

Correct or Incorrect?
The crying child is the most saddest child in the room.

Correct or Incorrect?
My pants were too short so I grew six inches since last year.

Correct or Incorrect?
The watermelons were ripe and ready to eat. YUM!

Correct or Incorrect?
We am going to the beach this summer.

Dictionary Skills

Put the following words in alphabetical order.

Alphabetical Order

1. dowdy   _____
    dolphin   _____
    dormouse   _____
    douse   _____

Alphabetical Order

2. fowl   _____
    foul   _____
    fossil   _____
    folklore   _____

Write the part of speech for each word and the root word and its part of speech. Then, fill in the blank in each sentence with the correct form of the root word.

3. *medicinal*   Part of Speech _____
    Root Word _____   Part of Speech _____

    • The soup I made tasted _____ and wasn't very good.

    • In order to get well, you need to take the _____ that the doctor prescribed.

4. *typically* Part of Speech _____

   Root Word _____ Part of Speech _____

- Yesterday was a _____ day and we did what we always do on Saturdays.

- On Saturdays, we _____ go to the grocery store, hang out with friends, and eat pizza.

5. *forgiving* Part of Speech _____

   Root Word _____ Part of Speech _____

- Tessa can usually _____ her little brother quickly since he's only three years old.

- Our dad is very _____ and always gives us a second chance.

Circle the words that would be on a dictionary page with the following guide words.

6. **navy**   **numb**

numerical

namesake

naysayer

neighborhood

novelty

numbness

nautical

Write sentences using two of the entry words listed above.

1. _____

_____

_____.

2. _____

_____

_____.

Introduction to Ecology Glossary

A

abundant—plentiful

acacia—a small tree that has yellow or white flowers (**acacias**)

alternative—another choice (**alternatives**)

anchored—held firmly in place

apex—the top point

B

bacteria—microscopic living things that exist everywhere; Some can be helpful and some can be harmful.

balance—in nature, the maintenance of populations in the proper amounts and conditions

C

coastline—the place where the land and the ocean meet

common—occurring often

conservationist—a person who works to protect animals, plants, and other natural resources (**conservationists**)

consumer—a living thing that eats other living things (**consumers**)

countless—too many to count

D

decay—to rot (**decaying**)

decompose—to rot, decay, or be slowly destroyed and broken down by natural processes (**decomposes**, **decomposed**)

decomposer—a living thing that eats dead plant and animal matter (**decomposers**)

defense—a way to protect against harm (**defenses**)

depend on—to rely on or need (**depends on**)

disaster—a sudden event that causes much damage or loss

E

ecology—the study of relationships between living things and their environment

ecosystem—everything in a particular environment, both living and nonliving

effect—a change resulting from influence or power (**effects**)

endangered—in danger of dying out completely

environment—natural surroundings (**environments**)

erode—to wear away over time due to wind or water (**erosion**, **eroded**)

extinction—a condition in which a kind of plant or animal dies out completely

F

flood—a condition in which a body of water rises and overflows beyond its usual limits (**floods**)

food chain—a relationship of living things as food sources for other living things (**food chains**)

force—something powerful, especially in nature (**forces**)

fragile—weak, easily harmed

fungus—a plant-like organism that lives on dead or decaying things (**fungi**)

G

gazelle—an antelope, or deer-like creature, that runs very fast (**gazelles**)

generate—to make (**generates**)

H

herd—a large group of animals (**herds**)

hydroelectric—using the power of water to make electricity

J

jackrabbit—an animal that looks like a large rabbit with long ears and long hind legs (**jackrabbits**)

L

landscape—an area of land that can be seen in one look

M

microscopic—can only be seen with a microscope

mighty—large in size

mineral—a substance that occurs naturally in some food and contributes to good health (**minerals**)

N

natural resource—a useful or valuable thing found in nature (**natural resources**)

naturalist—a person who studies living things in nature (**naturalists**)

nutrient—a vitamin or mineral that helps living things stay healthy (**nutrients**)

O

oil boom—a floating barrier put in water to keep oil from spreading (**oil booms**)

oil rig—a platform built above the ocean to support drilling for oil underwater

oil spill—an event during which oil is released into nature, usually into water, causing pollution

organic—from or made by living things

organism—a living thing

P

pasture—a field in which animals eat grass (**pastures**)

petrified—slowly changed into stone over time

photosynthesis—the process by which plants make their own food using sunlight

pollen—a yellow substance made by plants that is carried to other plants of the same kind to make seeds

polluted—dirty and unsafe

predator—an animal that lives by hunting other animals (**predators**)

prehistoric—a time before history was written down

prey—animals that are hunted by other animals for food

primarily—mainly

producer—a living thing that makes its own food (**producers**)

protect—to keep safe from harm

pump—to move liquid using a special machine

R

recover—to improve after an accident or difficult time

recycle—to process old things so they can be used again to make new things (**recycled, recycling**)

rely on—to depend on or need

reserve—an area of land where plants and animals are given special protection

reservoir—a lake in which water is stored for use

resource—something that is useful or valuable

S

safari—a trip taken to see or hunt wild animals

safety—the state of being free from harm

sapling—a young tree (**saplings**)

seal—to close up (**sealed**)

skitter—to move quickly across something (**skittering**)

soil—dirt

source—where something comes from

species—a group into which animals or plants are divided by scientists

sprout—to begin to grow

survival—the ability to continue living

survive—to continue living

T

technology—the invention of useful things or solving problems using science and engineering

topsoil—the top layer of soil that includes nutrients plants need

treasure—a valuable, important, or special thing (**treasures**)

U

unnecessary—not needed

upset—to interfere with

V

variety—a collection of different types

vitamin—a substance found in food that is necessary for good health (**vitamins**)

W

wander—to move around without a particular direction or purpose

wildebeest—a large, African antelope, or deer-like creature, with long, curving horns (**wildebeests**)

wilderness—a wild and natural area where no people live

wildlife—animals living in nature

Writing Prompts

Unit 11:

1. **Recommend** a way you can help protect and preserve the environment.

2. Describe food chains and provide several examples of food chains in nature.

3. **Decide** what the most important features of a forest ecosystem and a water ecosystem are and explain your choices.

4. Explain the chain of events related to an oil spill and how the environment is affected.

5. Write a letter to a friend telling about John Muir and what he did during his life to help the environment.

Either fiction or nonfiction:

1. Summarize the story or chapter you read in three to five sentences.

2. After reading this story or chapter, I wonder...

3. Name three things you liked about the story or chapter.

4. Make a timeline of three to five events in your reading today.

5. Pretend you are a TV reporter who has to interview the main character or person in the story or chapter you read, and write down five questions you would ask.

6. Make a prediction about what will happen next in the story or chapter you just read. Explain why you think this will happen.

7. Pretend you are the main character or a person in the story or chapter you read today and write a diary entry for that person.

8. Tell about something in the story or chapter you read today that is similar to something you have already read.

9. Draw a Venn diagram to show what is alike and/or different between two characters or people in the story or chapter you read.

10. How does the title fit the story or chapter? Suggest another title.

11. Write down three new words you learned while reading and tell what they mean. Use each word in a new sentence.

12. Name three questions you would ask the author of the story or chapter.

Fiction:

1. Tell about the setting.

2. Tell about the plot.

3. Tell about your favorite character. Write three reasons why you chose that character.

4. Which character is your least favorite? Write three reasons why you chose that character.

5. Give examples of personification from the story.

6. Draw a line down the center of your paper. On one side write the title of your favorite story. On the other side write the title of whatever you read today. Compare and contrast the main characters, the settings, and the plots.

7. Write a different ending for the story.

8. If you could be any character in the story or chapter you read today, who would you be? Give three reasons why.

9. Invent a conversation or dialogue between two characters or people in the story or chapter that you read. Write what each character says and don't forget to use quotation marks.

10. Describe a character, setting, or plot that surprised you. Explain what it was and why it surprised you.

11. Tell about a problem that someone in the story or chapter had and what he or she did about it.

Nonfiction:

1. Describe something that you learned from what you read today.

2. Write at least three questions you have after reading the chapter about the topic in the chapter.

Conference Record For Reader's Journal

Date: _____

Title of Book Student is Reading: _____

Is journal complete? Yes ____   No ____

Teacher notes:

Date: _____

Title of Book Student is Reading: _____

Is journal complete? Yes ____   No ____

Teacher notes:

Date: _____

Title of Book Student is Reading: _____

Is journal complete? Yes ____   No ____

Teacher notes:

Name: _____

Date: _____

Title of Book Student is Reading: _____

Is journal complete? Yes ____   No ____

Teacher notes:

Date: _____

Title of Book Student is Reading: _____

Is journal complete? Yes ____   No ____

Teacher notes:

Date: _____

Title of Book Student is Reading: _____

Is journal complete? Yes ____   No ____

Teacher notes:

CORE KNOWLEDGE LANGUAGE ARTS

SERIES EDITOR-IN-CHIEF
E. D. Hirsch, Jr.

PRESIDENT
Linda Bevilacqua

EDITORIAL STAFF
Carolyn Gosse, Senior Editor - Preschool
Khara Turnbull, Materials Development Manager
Michelle L. Warner, Senior Editor - Listening & Learning

Mick Anderson
Robin Blackshire
Maggie Buchanan
Paula Coyner
Sue Fulton
Sara Hunt
Erin Kist
Robin Luecke
Rosie McCormick
Cynthia Peng
Liz Pettit
Ellen Sadler
Deborah Samley
Diane Auger Smith
Sarah Zelinke

DESIGN AND GRAPHICS STAFF
Scott Ritchie, Creative Director

Kim Berrall
Michael Donegan
Liza Greene
Matt Leech
Bridget Moriarty
Lauren Pack

CONSULTING PROJECT MANAGEMENT SERVICES
ScribeConcepts.com

ADDITIONAL CONSULTING SERVICES
Ang Blanchette
Dorrit Green
Carolyn Pinkerton

ACKNOWLEDGMENTS

These materials are the result of the work, advice, and encouragement of numerous individuals over many years. Some of those singled out here already know the depth of our gratitude; others may be surprised to find themselves thanked publicly for help they gave quietly and generously for the sake of the enterprise alone. To helpers named and unnamed we are deeply grateful.

CONTRIBUTORS TO EARLIER VERSIONS OF THESE MATERIALS
Susan B. Albaugh, Kazuko Ashizawa, Nancy Braier, Kathryn M. Cummings, Michelle De Groot, Diana Espinal, Mary E. Forbes, Michael L. Ford, Ted Hirsch, Danielle Knecht, James K. Lee, Diane Henry Leipzig, Martha G. Mack, Liana Mahoney, Isabel McLean, Steve Morrison, Juliane K. Munson, Elizabeth B. Rasmussen, Laura Tortorelli, Rachael L. Shaw, Sivan B. Sherman, Miriam E. Vidaver, Catherine S. Whittington, Jeannette A. Williams

We would like to extend special recognition to Program Directors Matthew Davis and Souzanne Wright who were instrumental to the early development of this program.

SCHOOLS
We are truly grateful to the teachers, students, and administrators of the following schools for their willingness to field test these materials and for their invaluable advice: Capitol View Elementary, Challenge Foundation Academy (IN), Community Academy Public Charter School, Lake Lure Classical Academy, Lepanto Elementary School, New Holland Core Knowledge Academy, Paramount School of Excellence, Pioneer Challenge Foundation Academy, New York City PS 26R (The Carteret School), PS 30X (Wilton School), PS 50X (Clara Barton School), PS 96Q, PS 102X (Joseph O. Loretan), PS 104Q (The Bays Water), PS 214K (Michael Friedsam), PS 223Q (Lyndon B. Johnson School), PS 308K (Clara Cardwell), PS 333Q (Goldie Maple Academy), Sequoyah Elementary School, South Shore Charter Public School, Spartanburg Charter School, Steed Elementary School, Thomas Jefferson Classical Academy, Three Oaks Elementary, West Manor Elementary.

And a special thanks to the CKLA Pilot Coordinators Anita Henderson, Yasmin Lugo-Hernandez, and Susan Smith, whose suggestions and day-to-day support to teachers using these materials in their classrooms was critical.